Lillian Halegua was born in New York City and has lived in or around the city all her life. She has written eight novels, short stories, and also paints, sculpts and makes clothes and jewellery. She works as a librarian in Great Neck, NY State, and has completed a Masters degree in Library Science: 'I must feel secure in the knowledge that I can feed and clothe myself before I can return to the arts.'

About *The Pearl Bastard*:

'This story is not for the squeamish, who detest the sight of reality, but it is brilliantly written and a delicate subject is handled sensitively and understandingly, with a lyrical beauty that renders prose into poetry' *The Free Press*

'A short novel of tremendous impact and superb writing. Francie is one of the most vivid characters in modern fiction' *Los Angeles Mirror News*

LILLIAN HALEGUA

The
Pearl
Bastard

The Women's Press

TO SAMUEL

Published by The Women's Press Limited 1978
A member of the Namara Group
124 Shoreditch High Street, London E1 6JE

Reprinted 1985

First published in Great Britain
by Peter Owen Limited 1961

Copyright © Lillian Halegua 1959

Printed and bound in Great Britain by
Nene Litho and Woolnough Bookbinding
both of Wellingborough, Northants

British Library Cataloguing in Publication Data

Halegua, Lillian
    The Pearl Bastard
    I. Title
    813'.54[F]   PS3558.A35/

    ISBN 0-7043-3828-9

Part
One

*C*alm, calm sea. Old sea. I will be peaceful as the sea. Browned and battered by the wind. Creased as the ripples of the water floor. Stone smooth, smooth as the gull. Silver smooth, gliding as the gull.

I will be as the sea. I will be as the sea and the wind and the stones and the white winged gulls. Poor white winged gull. I will stick to the sea. Safe with the sea. Silver flashes dropping to the sea.

He said, never stopping, "That's what you call knocking the shit out of something."

Plastered white, and the wipers smeared the guts across the window. Looking back to see the broken white and the cars. And the car never stopping, never slowing, even for the striking thud. Hairy knuckles, hairy fingers held the wheel and held the road, riding, riding. Bowels splashed against the windshield for the remembering.

I sat. He would not stop the car. I sat and gagged and could not jump for the speed. Swallowing hard, not to vomit in this car with the polished green. Green and a strip of gold shooting down the side. White tires and chrome and leatherlike seats, green seats and a clock, time on a dashboard and buttons making music. Music, with the wind blowing in cool and salty and the music blowing out. Streamers of sound, oral ribbons in the wind.

Sea gull sounds, high note singing, soothing. And I cannot cry for a dead sea gull. Insides sick and I could not eat and I could not cry.

He said, "Hey! You want a bite?" and swerved round and stopped fast so I was standing and then thrown back hard against the green leather, but I did not splash against the seat like the gull against the glass.

He did not know my name. "Hey!" he called me and it was okay.

"Hey! You want a bite?" he said and his head was as black as the hair on his arms, only more, thick black, straight like short black wires. Hands unloosed from the wheel, thick dark hairy hands, nails black as the hairs that crept down the fingers.

"I got!" and pointed to the brown paper bag. The door slammed and the bag shook and crinkled and he was gone.

I smelled the smells of cooking oil and almost heard the burgers sizzling on the grill through the silver rippled walls and the greasy windows. The salami smelled strong from the bag and I almost reached in and bit, but my eyes would not leave the window. I could not bite. In the stillness it was not white, just red and green and brown and grey running together, caking in the sun on the windshield and my eyes would not turn and I could not eat.

Black strip of tar, winding tar. Dead grey white and blood red on the black tar and wheels, turning wheels, turning wheels, breaking feathers, breaking slender bones, crushing against the hard black tar. A bird is not a bird to lie buried in a box. Birds to the earth, to the worms. Gulls to the sea, to the fish. Not to wheels, not to the speeding, spinning wheels.

It did not cry out or scream, just a sharp loud crack and nothing. It did not cry and I would not cry but I could not sit and see the flies swarming at the glass. Gulls belong to be buried in the sea.

I got out and took the paper bag.

"Hey! Hop in!" he called and I turned and saw the bottle sweating cold in his hand and my tongue was thick and dry. It would be a long walk back and the gravel dry, cut into my sneakers. It was too late anyway. Nothing to bury but the scrapings.

The bottle cold against my hands and wet and cool running down my tongue. Bubbles ran down and burned against my chest and up in one loud bubble. He heard, but he did not say and I drank slowly, saving, making it last with the ride.

The bottle crashed loud and struck and splintered against hard tar.

"Hey kid! You crazy? You wanna get me fined? Wanna guy's tires to blow?"

This guy worrying for a hunk of rubber. Rubber ain't got a soul. Gulls have. Tires patch and grow round with air. Men worry for a tire, worry for the money a tire costs. Gulls are cheap, free to watch, free to fly. Gulls are cheap, cheaper than a rubber tube.

Black hairy hands and blackened nails must've changed a load of tires. Mine were white and thin, whiter than his even though I didn't wash all day.

"Skinny, scrawny," Pa said. They are thin and strong and hard. Good strong hands that rubbed the rubbing wash. Strong hands, strong for scrubbing floors.

Sucking the little finger. The man said, "Baby!" Always good and warm it tastes and it is not baby, not like the thumb anyways.

I started to tell about the little finger but he did not look, he did not care. Even Ma don't know about the little finger. Ma knows about how I screamed when I was just a baby and her cooing and me screaming until she saw Caroline had my hand and was biting hard and my pinky almost hung in her mouth. Little finger, it did not grow, but it is not ugly. It is small and I let the nail grow and keep it clean and filed.

Jealous Caroline. Whining Caroline. I don't

care how many babies Ma has and she does. Ma never saw the little finger. Ma never noticed.

Ma said, "Write and let us know." Ma said, "Be good and don't trust strangers." Ma said, "Be back before school starts. Be back good and healthy with meat on them bones. Save your money and don't work too hard. Save your money and send a little home." Ma cried a little.

Caroline said, "Why can't she work here like me and Jimmy and the rest? Why she gotta go so far? Montauk's far, Ma! It's not just over the bridge like Astoria. It's a long way and Francie's dumb. Ma, Francie's real stupid for such a big girl."

Jealous Caroline. But Ma knew Caroline was afraid she'd have to loan me a dress because Ma said I should look like a girl. And Ma knew I got the sea in me like Uncle Louie. Ma said, "Maybe she can get a job sticking fish in cans or pasting labels." Maybe Ma thought the smell of so much fish would finish the sea for me.

Ma said, "Don't go with boys. You're too young for boys."

I wouldn't go with boys that way. Not flirting and gushing like the way of Caroline. I like boys but not that way. I mean for friends I like them, not like a giggling girl.

I didn't wear Caroline's dress or her shoes or her anything. Jimmy loaned his shirt, nice and white and he ironed it smooth and Ma rolled the cuffs neat to my elbows and I rolled them higher till they wouldn't roll no more. Ma said to wear my jumper at least. She said she would even unstitch the St. Agnes High label but I swore I wouldn't wear it after school ended. I swore it.

I like the feel of jeans, rough and stiff and hard against my skin. I can cross my legs and stick my feet up high and nothing shows. I wear the kind that Jimmy wears, with the waist low and easy and the zipper sliding up and down the front.

Ma said, "Don't go with boys, you're too young for boys."

Sometimes I'm one with them and I think I am more boy than girl. Really boy, like my arms are hard and strong.

"Skinny, scrawny," Pa said. "Get a good hot lunch," he said and handed me a five. I know what he meant. He meant for carfare and things and just in case something went wrong I'd have some money. He meant not to spend it fast and save a little and count my change and be careful not to lose it. I could feel it plain under my toe, whole and unbroken and waiting under my toe.

A pocketful of coins jingling when I put my fingers in and swished. A five stuck waiting under my toe. I took the bus across the bridge and then I stood and watched the cars go by and waved my thumb until a car slowed and I ran running down the road.

The lady in the Buick with the fuzzy bleachy hair said, "Are you a boy or a girl?" and I said girl. I shouldn't have. I should have said boy and saved myself a lecture. Who wants long hair streaming in your eyes and itching on your neck?

She said, "I wish I had your color. I wish I had your waves."

If I could I'd give the blondness, the waves away. The only waves I want are the ones bursting from the sea.

Till coming to the Island I saw the waves but once. Once at Coney. Once when we were small and Caroline wore a table cloth and tucked it here and pinned it there and called it a tropic sarong

8

and it kept getting undone and she couldn't get it wet in the water.

Pa said I was skinny, scrawny as a boy and nobody would know the difference. I was only eight or nine and Paul's old trunks were big even with the string pulled tight. I kept my arms folded high, all day folded high across my chest.

High was Mama's dress, high above her knees till the edge of her bloomers showed, and her legs thick and white, veined and knotted in purple blue, kicked at the water and splashed.

The water filled with kicking and splashing. Pushing everywhere. I went out to where the water touched my chin and it felt good and clean and the waves, small kindly waves, bobbed me up and down. I felt cool and good and clean, even though we all let out in the water, I felt clean.

I smelled the salt in the wind all the time, even though I saw the ocean only once. And I felt the hot sand burning at my feet and the wet smooth sand at the water's edge and the sea weeds curling round my toe. I kept seeing sand though I saw little of the sand so long ago.

Bodies, bodies, bodies, sprawled on top, covering people sitting, lying, standing, walking, kicking sand and there was no room. No room, and more and more came out and pushed into the mass of people and spread their blankets until you couldn't walk straight with the heads and arms and legs.

You could not build a castle for all the feet walking. I dug a hole, small deep hole and there was water at the bottom. In the park at home in the Bronx I dug lots of holes and there was never water in the bottom. Only earth and ants and worms and I sat and watched the worms wriggling and the worms made me think of fish.

I found a shell on the beach. Shiny smooth it was, white with rainbow colors spreading out. Jimmy said you could hear the sea from a shell. I put my ear to the shell but I could hear nothing but the throb of my hand. My shell was too small. Small and shiny and rainbowy it was. Jimmy wanted to drill a hole and run a ribbon through so I could wear it round my neck. I did not need a hole to pierce my shell and break my rainbow. I carried it tight in my hand and never let go. My teacher said it was mother-of-pearl and I could not understand how this small smooth thing could be the mother of anything.

Ma lifted her dress and walked in till the water touched her knees. Jimmy splashed and Ma laughed and splashed back and her dress came loose from her hands and the hem floated on the water. Ma wrung and wrung and when it dried all the wringing creases stayed and it looked pretty bad on the train back to the city.

On the train Pa turned red and redder and his feet swelled and he had to leave the laces off his shoes and pull the flaps out so they wouldn't touch the skin. Lucky he only rolled his pants to the calves so he could bend his knees if not his feet. I was burnt to my belly except where I kept folding my arms. Tired we were, but we could not sleep for the burning or the vinegar smell or the fighting.

Pa said it was Ma's fault that he was burnt because it was Ma that wanted to go and kept nagging and nagging. Pa said the beach was nothing but sweating niggers and overstuffed Jews and now he was suffering for taking us all to the beach like Ma kept asking.

Ma said it was no picnic for her with the looking after all the kids and wiping their noses and packing the lunch and counting us all the day.

Caroline said that Ma had nothing to complain about because she was the one who got stuck with the looking after the little ones and it was she who was the one who should complain.

Caroline was sore because she couldn't flirt much with the kids dragging along.

And Ma said Caroline was a no good tramp and other names and Ma forgot to fight with Pa while she had Caroline to contend with and Caroline came in and pushed me over right on my sunburn and crawled in and covered her head with the blankets even though it was so hot.

My arm freckled and burned out the window of the new green car, but the wind came in blowing and cooled the burn and I did not take my arm in off the window because it felt so good.

That man, I bet he doesn't burn with his dark skin.

Ma said, "Never trust a stranger," and I wasn't

trusting him. I sat all the way over, right smack against the door with the brown paper bag between, until the salami smelled so strong I put it down on the floor near the door so the smell would not be too much for him.

With the smell, I was sorry I took salami. Ma said for me to take cheese, but salami tastes good in my mouth and I did not dream I would be riding in this kind of car. With the smell, I was sorry for stinking up his car and him nice enough to pick me up and take me all the way out. He was going all the way to the Point and I never figured on seeing the Point so quick.

He was quiet and his Ford was new and slick. It was not like riding in the beat up Buick with the fuzzy blonde. She was all questions, wanting to know my name and where I came from and where I was going and why. She was the one giving the lift and I had to be polite and answer and tell her how many we were and the names of the seven boys and the three girls. You'd think we were freaks or something the way she carried on. She said she felt sorry for Ma. Caroline would have had a laugh. Caroline thinks it's terrible because she has to take care of all the rest while Ma takes care of the new one. I think it is worse to do the washing and the floors, especially the bathroom because Roger and Amos never aim right.

Ma said I should do girl's work and washing is not for girls. I was supposed to do the ironing and the mending, and Jimmy the floors and the wash. But the iron makes me hot and sweaty and my sewing was not so hot and I had them all hollering, even Pa about the lumps in his socks. Jimmy didn't much like the floors or the washing. The diapers and the hairs on the floor made him sick to his stomach, so we switched.

The wind blew in and rippled the silky stuff of his sleeve against his arm. It looked like the kind of soft stuff that would be smooth underneath next to your skin, and I almost wanted to reach out and stroke the smoothness.

I didn't. I didn't want to get so friendly with a man I did not know. He wasn't friendly, never spoke, never said his name or asked me mine. He drove me out and bought the soda and said I could stay in the motel with the fancy green and yellow spreads.

At home we have curtains up on the windows but we have no spreads. Ma is tatting one out of fine white stuff. Ma said it would be done by the time the littlest one is married, then she can settle down and fix up the rooms and use the spread she has been working on so long. Irish lace, she calls it and it looks like coarse white spider webbing.

Pa said it was all foolishness and just a way to waste his money because tatting takes balls and balls and balls of this fine white stuff.

Once this man who was driving said, "Balls!" and I did not like it but I said nothing and made believe I did not hear. He was driving along straight and fast and a car shot out of a small side road. He swerved, and I swung my head down between my knees and then we were riding smooth and easy again. Maybe he thought I couldn't hear because my head was down so low or maybe he figured me for a boy and boys curse.

Jimmy uses plenty of curse words. He says balls all the time and worse too. He says f— when Ma and Pa aint around to hear him. He says f— very often.

This motel he wanted to share had a shower and a toilet and a sink and two beds and a desk and a big mirror and a closet and a chest of drawers and a carpet on the floor and a boiler that stood in the bathroom so you could have plenty of hot water and it had pictures on the wall. Pictures of fish and a whale, I guess the whale picture was for the name of a motel. WAILING WHALE the sign said and two pink pole lamps stood in front and we drove up a hill to number eight.

He said, "Don't cost me nothing more if you should stay."

He paid twelve bucks for that place and the sign said the room had to be vacant by twelve noon and it was just past seven o'clock and he wouldn't even have that place for one full day.

Twelve bucks! That is almost what we pay a week back home and we have five rooms and a kitchen. Not so fancy as this, but twelve bucks!

I could almost tell by the sign outside that this was a take-your-money kind of place. The sign said, MOTEL, COCKTAILS, BREAKFAST, LUNCH, DINNER, FINEST SEAFOOD, COLD BEER and REAL ESTATE.

A lady came out and she was Brooklyn. Real Brooklyn. She was dumb Brooklyn and he was dumber saying the room was fine and then asking how much.

He didn't say nothing when I left and I didn't say nothing. I walked down the hill past the two pink lanterns and saw the water and the sky and the clouds. A sign said WAILING WHALE PRIVATE BEACH and it was private, nobody around as far as I could see. All the way up and down the beach nothing except the gulls and me.

This was nothing like Coney. I don't mean the no people. I mean the beach and the kind of sand and the stones and the small white fences stuck in the sand. I kind of knew people with a motel and a bar and a restaurant wouldn't have time to take care of a beach. The beach was dotted with rusty beer cans and sea weed and a broken wooden crate and a tree trunk that must've been washed ashore a long while back because it was all dry and rotting.

I kind of stood and looked and felt all funny like I was taking communion or graduating or something. I took my sneakers off and rolled up the cuffs of my jeans. I left the five in the toe of my sneaker because there was no place else. Ma and

Caroline hide money in brassieres but I did not need to wear one yet.

The water was cold, real cold on my toes and I jumped back. I played a game of jumping in and getting cold and jumping out. Then I didn't get so cold, only cool and walked in further and further. The water was clean and clear, so clear I could see my toes and the stones that dug into the soles of my feet.

Waves came in and wet my pants. I wet my hands and dripped the water down my arms, on my face, in my hair. The water ran cold down my neck, down my back, wetting the clean white shirt that Jimmy did up so well.

Too bad Jimmy does not like the sea, like me. We could have been here together. Maybe it's better because I do not like to talk when I like something. I like it still, quiet still, just right for dreaming. Jimmy likes to talk, not stupid things like Caroline, Jimmy never says stupid things but he likes to talk.

I felt the water come up high and watched the gulls swoop down catching fish and stared at the sun and the clouds and the boats that passed and the boats that pulled into the dock that I could see all the way down the beach.

I never saw the wave. It came in fast and high and I did not have time to see the white, it pulled my feet out, feet up with the wave and I was down with the rocks. I was scared, plenty scared, scrambling and falling and breathing in the salty water. My eyes wet and burning and my feet cutting on the stones, trying to get straight, pushing my hands against the stones to pull me up. The wave pushed out to sea and I was out of the water, wet out of the water. Water in my eyes and my ears and my throat, in my lungs, dripping down my face from my hair. Coughing, choking, sputtering up plenty of water, plenty scared.

I could have drowned with no one to see me on the beach and I can't swim. Everybody knows how to swim, I know, except me. One time in the water at Coney couldn't teach me. In the bathtub, it was too small and it was always bumping elbows. I could have drowned and no one would know. I was plenty scared.

Scared and chilled, my arm all goose fleshed and me having to go from the scare and the chill. I thought of going back to number eight to use his toilet, but maybe he would say to take off the wet things and then he'd know I wasn't a boy. While I was thinking it came out wet and warm and mingled with the other wet that ran down my legs and made puddles in the sand. It was nothing so bad. There were no bushes, no place to hide, to go. No one on the beach, but it was all open and I felt eyes on my back and could not let my pants down. No one could tell with my pants so wet but I felt ashamed like everyone knew.

I stood to let the wind blow on the wet. Soon the dripping stopped and my hair was almost dry, only my pants felt heavy like a ton of iron was hanging from my hips.

I sat and let the sand cake across my bottom and watched the gulls and the waves. I began to like the rusty cans against the sand. It made me wonder who it was who stayed out here and drank the beer. The cans had a coppery rust, pocked and corroded by the beach, some half buried peeping through like rounded rusting stones. And the old wood box stood on its long end like someone used it for a stool, but I don't think they really did. The nails were rusty and the slats thin and whitened, bleached by the sun and the salt, and some of the slats were broken and hung down and rocked in the wind. Maybe once it was an orange crate, but now it wasn't craty, the wood was smooth like it was sandpapered a million times.

It was good to have come all the way out here. At first I only said I was going and Caroline said Ma would never let me and I said she would, and then I begged and begged till I got Ma to say yes and then I had to go.

Jimmy was really sorry, not jealous sorry, and he could have come too but he got this job at Dewey the butcher's and Ma said it was a chance for him to learn a trade. Butchers make a lot of money, she says, but it is not girl's work. Anyway I know Jimmy wouldn't like it here. It is too quiet for Jimmy. Jimmy likes noise and lots of people and dancing. Jimmy doesn't like the quiet or the sea.

It was good I had come because this was better than the five and ten. Summer it is hot in the five and ten and people yelling, "Miss! Miss!" makes it even hotter. You say, "Don't smear the lipstick on your hand!" and they do it anyway. Counting change is hot, like taking sixty-nine from seventy-five or adding taxes.

The sun was not hot any more. It was a big red ball sliding down the water. And the water was black, before it was so blue and now it was black with silver shots and a long narrow path of red to the sun. Red carpet to the sun and if you didn't know you would almost think it was real and leading to the sun. If I could skim the water as a fish or had a boat with a motor on the back I would take that road, take it quick and smooth, straight out to that big red ball lying on the water.

A white boat came by the sun covered by a cloud. Then I saw that it was no cloud but a great white mass of gulls. The gulls flew close to the boat like pigeons on a roof. The boat came closer to the dock and the gulls came too, following.

I wondered if anyone ever caught a gull and caged it like a canary. I know this lady who has about a hundred birds in her house. All you have to do is say you like birds and she takes you in and lets you see all the birds in their cages. She's got all kinds, green and yellow and big and small, singing and talking and one that even meows like a cat. Even if you're just walking by you can hear them. Once I went and she was nice and showed me through the rooms. She had all shapes of velvety chairs with fancy lacy scarves on the arms and backs and dolls sitting all over them and cages, cages, cages all over up to the ceiling almost. In some there were lots of birds together in one cage and they screamed and shrieked and peeped and talked and she tried to get one to say my name but it didn't. It kept screaming, "Shut up! Shut up!" and I wanted to scream, "Shut up" too, but I didn't.

Amos goes often, she gives you candy if you stay looking at those birds long enough.

I wonder if she had a gull where she would keep it. In the bathtub with chicken wire all around? Poor gull. Poor poor birds.

The wind blew and it got cool and I rolled down my sleeves and buttoned the cuffs but it was still cool. I was getting hungry. I had forgotten all about eating out there on the beach and in the car I was ashamed for that man to see.

The salami tasted good. It was hard and tasty and plenty spicy. The rolls were getting stale and crumbs fell down and stuck to the damp dungarees. It is nice to eat when you are alone and dreaming and no one is watching. Then the stuff goes down easy and tastes good and before you know it it is gone and you are wanting more. I cannot stand to eat at school where everyone watches and stares at what you eat like their eyes are between the bread of your sandwich. Once when I was in public school, a girl, she was Jewish, brought matzos. I think I would have eaten in the bathroom with all the stinking than out there with all the staring.

That time when I was small and out at Coney, I didn't eat all that day. You couldn't with all those people staying right on top of you almost. A kid with big eyes watched Jimmy eat his egg till Jimmy had to turn his back and shove the whole thing in his mouth before the kid quit watching.

Ma handed out hard boiled eggs and tomatoes and rolls and watermelon. I remember I took an egg and when I got it all peeled I couldn't put it in

24

my mouth. I stuck it back in the bag and **Ma** never knew I didn't eat. I wasn't hungry either. I was too excited watching all the things. The water this way and the boardwalk that way and all the people walking and sitting and being wheeled in big straw chairs on the boardwalk. And the parachute jump. Parachutes going up high with people sitting in them. Slowly they went up and when it came to the top the chute jumped and came down fast. Great white umbrellas shooting down and you could see the feet dangling from the seats and hear the screams.

I didn't get hungry until the man with the ice cream came. He came sweating, red, over the arms and legs, bent double with his load. Stopping and opening the box as the people called and I could see the pops and the cups and the sandwiches all lined up neat and the steaming cold coming from the ice. Ma said to ask Pa because he had all the money, but Pa walked away over to the Life Guard stand. At first Jimmy followed but then he turned back and kicked the sand and a fat lady hollered. Ma and Caroline pretended that he did not belong to them until the lady stopped her hollering.

Ma never fights with neighbors over kids. Ma is respectable and tried to make us respectable too. Ma never called us through the window or hit us in the street. Ma never let us eat bread or anything in the street. Ma said it wasn't nice to get others wanting and she couldn't afford to be feeding the whole entire neighborhood.

The whole block likes Ma and gives Ma all the outgrown baby things. We got boxes of tiny dresses and nightgowns and blankets and diapers, diapers, diapers. We used diapers when we were out of towels, that's how many diapers. Ma buys every baby a brand new bib. When Ma gets that way she goes out shopping from store to store till she finds the nicest, prettiest, most best for her money bib.

Ma has the prettiest babies. Whenever Ma comes home from the hospital the whole block comes up to see. Caroline says they come with hopes of seeing a dud. But Ma's never had a homely baby. I never saw Paul or Caroline or Jimmy or me and I don't remember Edna so well but all the rest have been sweet and blonde and fat. We've got the fattest, healthiest babies and Ma said that was because they never touched milk bought from a store.

They don't all stay so pretty when they grow. Amos was real nice until he lost his teeth and the new ones that grew in never stopped growing and went right on growing past his lip. Roger was the only red headed baby and Ma let the curls grow down his neck and Pa and Jimmy and Paul were sore but Ma wouldn't let no one cut it. When Ma was having Torrence, Paul took Roger to the barber's and Ma never forgave him. Whenever Ma saw Roger with his hair straight and falling in his eyes she'd say, "That fool! That damned fool Paul!"

Ma said she had the best looking family in the world. I think some of us are and some of us aren't. I could never be pretty like Caroline. Caroline is lipstick and curlers pretty and something sweet from a bottle that makes it tickle all the way up my nose.

It made Ma nervous that Caroline was always washing and brushing and fixing herself up. Pa took the lock off the bathroom door, so the rest could get in and not have to stand and hammer at the door. Caroline was sore and she wouldn't leave her soap or toothpaste on the shelf no more. Caroline was sore at Pa and sore at Amos, always hollering at Amos because he would not learn to knock. Amos will never learn to knock.

Caroline dressed at Mrs. Finney's when she went out on Saturday night. It was better for Ma, it didn't make her so nervous with all the fussing and the running back and forth. After Caroline goes out Mrs. Finney comes up and tells Ma what she wore and how she looked and if the boy was nice and what he does and what he wore and what he said. Nosey Mrs. Finney. I would die if I were a boy having to call for a girl at Mrs. Finney's.

I know why Caroline went to Mrs. Finney's. It was not so much to dress or because of no lock on the bathroom door. Caroline was ashamed for boys to come when Ma was having babies.

Ma said it was more respectable to have babies than not to. Ma said she didn't have to be ashamed to look God in the eye like some of those others. Ma said it was more important to listen to God than the neighbors' wisecracks.

Caroline didn't care what Ma said, she said as soon as she graduated she was getting out. Caroline said she would move to Manhattan and live in a hotel and never have to cook or clean. Caroline said she would come to visit but not very often and if we wanted we could meet her for lunch or go to a show with her downtown.

I'm not much for eating out with so many people all around. I'm not much for the show either. Jimmy likes the show. Jimmy would like the eating with the people all around. Jimmy likes people and people like Jimmy. Everyone knows Jimmy. The whole neighborhood knows Jimmy. They know him to say hello and his name. Jimmy knows names too. Jimmy can remember an awful lot of names.

Ma likes it when Jimmy's home. Ma always laughs with Jimmy. Sometimes they push back the table and dance. Jimmy tells Ma how good she is and Ma tells how good she was when she was young and how much dancing she always did and about the fellows who couldn't tire her out and how she loved to jig and whirl and about the dresses she wore and the shoes and how her hair was all tied up and things like that. Remembering, sometimes she laughed, sometimes she cried, remembering, and it made Pa uneasy.

Ma said she used to dance as good as Jimmy.

Then her legs got all swollen and veined and it was hard for her to dance.

Jimmy dances all of the time. When he's walking or running or even just standing he's dancing, snapping his fingers and moving his knees and tapping and shuffling and clapping and swinging round and jumping and snapping his heels together and beating rhythms against the sidewalk with the heels and the soles of his shoes. He's always beating on walls and tables and fences with his fingers or sticks, not just banging but rhythms, all kinds of rhythms. The rhythms come out of his arms and legs filling the air with sounds and I walk quiet, listening. Deep inside I feel the rhythms too but they stay inside. I feel the beating, all kinds of beatings, but mine don't come out, mine are only for me to hear and nobody knows. All the world knows Jimmy's. Not all the world, I mean the Highbridge section in the Bronx all know Jimmy and he makes them smile and hum and come right out and clap their hands.

Jimmy isn't even still when he sleeps. Jimmy had to sleep by himself on a cot because no one could stand the thrashing. His legs jerk under the covers and his arm goes out all of a sudden and his body jumps like you do when you dream that you're falling, only Jimmy says he never dreams.

I was sitting on the beach thinking if Jimmy would like it here and how he wouldn't like to be a butcher because seeing blood makes him sick to his stomach. Jimmy couldn't wear no blood stained apron or walk on sawdust or stand all day in a narrow aisle behind a counter. Jimmy needs a stage and music and people watching. Ma said Jimmy needed to learn a trade and butchers make money. Butchers even make more money than cops or mail men. Butchers get their aprons free and their meat. Ma said it would be good to get free meat.

I was feeling bad for Jimmy, sitting on that beach getting cold. I should've taken a sweater. Ma said to take a sweater. Ma said to take a lot of things. Ma got out Edna's Christmas pajamas and Caroline's drawers and Paul's heavy sweater and Caroline's toweling robe and my socks and my school white blouse and a couple of diapers for when my girl friend came. She filled a great big grocery bag and I wasn't going to drag that bag around all over Long Island. Ma started to nag about taking the bag and I had to get out without saying a real goodbye.

I could have used Paul's heavy sweater. The wind came in blowing over the water. Cold blowing over the water and the sun was down. My sleeves were down but that didn't help much. The shirt was damp and sticking to my skin and my pants were wet and stiff.

I rubbed my arms to get the goose flesh down and thought I'd stand and run up and down the beach to get my blood running warm.

I stood and saw the man coming towards the beach carrying beer. My eyes saw the beer cans, one in each hand, and my tongue dried and swole and almost hung out and licked the wind.

Shivering with the beer. Teeth chattering with the beer. I felt him drop to the sand but I was busy drinking. Drinking and shivering and chattering.

He wore no shirt, no shoes, only pants. Light blue that clung to his waist unbelted and blew against his legs with the wind. Light blue like light blue sails blowing. He was like a sailor with his arms tattooed. Tanned, strong, hairy arms against the blue. There was no blue except the blue that flapped against his legs.

The water dark, dark grey or black and the sky dark and clouded, white grey and pink. And the gulls singing, white and silver. There was no blue except his blue and he lay flat on the sand, the wiry hairs touching sand, right besides me in the sand. I set the can against the sand and rubbed the moist cold from my hands. My tongue was wet and right again with beer. It was good beer. It was cold beer. I tasted beer before with Pa. Pa with the foaming bucket, beer from the barrel, good clear amber from the barrel and pretzels, salty pretzels in a bowl on the bar. I filled my pockets full of pretzels and Pa carried the bucket, careful not to spill. The white foam stayed on top, moving like the waves but there was no sloshing. I liked the foam best, bitter foam licked against my tongue. Pa let me have the foam, glass half full of foam to put some meat on skin and bones.

Ma drank beer for the babies, and the babies grew fat on the beer that ran out milk from the breasts that hung full from my mother.

The man lay still and tan against the sand. I

wondered if he'd speak and if he did, what to say. If he asked my name I'd say Frankie, like when I was small Jimmy called me Frankie. I tried to call Jimmy Geranium like he wanted. It was hard to say, to remember, and I did not like those pots against the window. The leaves felt fuzzy and smelled a funny smell when I touched them, but Jimmy liked that name and I tried remembering to call him what he liked.

This man, I did not know his name, should have a strong man's name like Hercules or Geronimo or Goliath. He was not cold with the cold, his arms were smooth hard and brown, not bumped with cold and his chest was warm with matted hair, black wiry curls and his nipples were pink and soft, not pimpled nipples with the cold.

I could feel the tips of mine pushing at my shirt. Shivering, teeth chattering, covering the tips with my arms, still shivering.

The man said, "You cold, kid?"

I could not answer with the wind knocked out. I could not scream or kick. He rolled over and knocked me flat and swung on top. His hands pushed my head into sand and his mouth stayed on my ear, licking, biting.

I could not breathe for the heaviness, pushing, pushing against the heaviness.

I tried to say I was not cold or say get off or scream but his mouth was there and his tongue would not let the words come out. Knees pushing against knees, hands beneath my shirt, grabbing, pulling, mauling on my pants, tearing.

It was like the sea that knocked me off my feet. It was like the sea that surged and pounded and broke in and out in waves. Pushed down drowning in this sea. Burning, hurting with the power of this sea.

Part

Two

The sky rumbled and I did not hear. Drops came down, large cold drops that splashed against my skin and I hardly felt them splash. I could feel him breathing hard somewhere in the dark.

He said, "C'mon before it pours!"

But I would not listen, would not answer to his rasping voice.

He said, "The hell with you!" and I could hear him scramble up the beach.

I was quiet, lying quiet, hardly breathing. I did not want to breathe no more. I would not let my lungs let out, lying still, chest hurting and I hardly felt this hurt with all the other hurt.

Splitting noise of thunder, crashing thunder and the sky lit up with lightning and the rain came running down.

Crashes, loud crashes of the thunder and my mouth held open screaming out against the thunder. The rain came down and beat against my flesh. The rain ran down my mouth and washed my tongue and gurgled in my throat with the screams. Tears running with the wet of the rain and the screams. Beating my hands against the sand, knuckles hurting with the hard of stones. Fists hurting, hurting more than all the rest.

The waves beat against the beach with the wind. The lightning came and snapped against the sea. Shining, angry, snapping, lighting up the sea and the sky and I hoped the streaks would come down fast to me.

"Hit me! Hit me!" I cried, waiting for the hit, the burn.

"God, let it hit! God, let it hit!" I screamed, screaming loud at God but the thunder drowned the screams.

"Jesus, Jesus, let me die!" but Jesus would not hear.

Crying, still crying when the thunder stopped and the sky stayed dark. Crying low in the quiet of the rain, throat aching from the screams. Still and quiet crying with just the wet running from my eyes like there was a sea of wet to keep running from my eyes.

The wind died, stopping the pounding of the water on the beach, just a gentle slapping left. The rain slowed to a thin fine stream, cold stream and the air was cold. Cold air. Freezing cold in the no wind rain. In the slapping of the sea I heard the gulls and the ringing of the buoy. The gentle slapping of the sea and the gentle singing and the long low ringing of the buoy.

I did not belong with this sea. Freezing with this sea.

I wrapped my shirt around my shoulders and grabbed my sneakers and my dungarees and ran cutting my feet on the stones, stubbing my toes on the slats of the small wood fence.

The sign lit up the road. The great neon sign blinking in and blinking out, the sign of the WAIL-

ING WHALE. The two pink poles lit up the drive that led up the road to number eight.

I ran from the road and the sign, running down the road towards the dark, away from the sign and the posts and the drive up the hill and number eight. The light pushed out and stabbed my back. Stabbing, stabbing, and the shadows ran and jumped in the light that came stabbing against my back.

I saw the shadow of a house and made for the house and crouched near the walls, flat against the walls of the house to feel the warmth. But the wall was cold and wet and it was not warm like a house is warm inside, only wet and cold and I stayed freezing near the wall.

A dog barked and a voice called, "Who's there?" The dog barked more and more, loud excited barking dog, and I crouched close to the house and listened to the barks and listened to the voice demanding, "Who's out there?" crouching in the dark.

The light came round from a ball, round and out from a ball and hot on my face, hot on me with my dungarees on my arm and my sneakers in my hand and the light burned my eyes shut in my face.

"You're the kid from number eight!" It was the Brooklyn sound from the lady of the motel.

"What you doing here? What d'you want? What you doing without clothes on? What you doing in this rain, in this cold without no clothes?"

On and on with the light burning in my face hurting my eyes and I couldn't say. I couldn't say with the light. I couldn't say, couldn't see her face, not standing, not sitting, against the wall and her voice came in and out, squeaking in and out with the light.

"You cold? You sick? You lost? You dead?"

The dog was out, barking, jumping.

"Stop Fido!" and she dragged me round the waist and I leaned limp against the soft flab while she dragged.

"You cold? You hurt? You hungry?" and the blankets felt rough and scratched against my skin and the coffee perked and steamed and smelled strong and good to my nose.

"Caught in the storm? Boat wreck? Car crackup?"

The coffee burned against my lip. My lip swole and cut with his hard sharp teeth. My hands shook and the coffee sloshed and spilled down burning on my chin.

"Where's that man you were with? That man your father? He hurt or dead or something?"

I shook my head and it would not stop shaking. It turned round and round on my neck and the room turned round with it and the lady turned and turned in the turning room.

Somewhere in the turning I said, "I don't belong to him." Somewhere in the turning I swallowed small white pills and drank a burning drink and heard her say "Sleep. Go to sleep," and I heard her say "to sleep" in my sleep.

In the sleeping there was dreaming and I was falling, falling, waking with the jumping and the covers choking. Waking, shaking from the sleep and dropping back. I saw his face and the gull and I was the gull while he squashed me with his foot and I could not spread my wings and fly. I just stayed staring at the foot that came down stamping.

I could not shake the foot or the dream. I slept dying like the gull. Hurt and broken like the gull in my sleep.

I felt wet on my face and thought it was the sea, a wave washing up and washing me. It was good to be washed clean by a wave. Then I smelled the smell of food and heard the clink of cups and coffee perking in a pot and bacon sizzling. The wave came up and washed some more and the wave was the tongue of the dog.

My eyes all swollen and my lips and my hands.

She said, "Can you stand?" She said, "Use ice on your face." She said, "Come and eat."

The ice squares burned against my lips and eyes. The water pained my hands. The cuts on the back of my hands were filled with dirt. With the edge of a towel I scrubbed away the dirt. The cuts began to bleed and I pressed the ice down hard till my hands burned from the cold and not the cuts.

I never tasted bacon and eggs so good or coffee so strong, real good strong coffee.

The woman waited till I was half way through before she started, "What happened to you last night? What were y'doing with that guy in number eight? Where you from? What y'doing here? How old are you?"

Then I told her about the man in the green car giving me a ride right out to the Point and how I was fifteen and how I came out here to get a job and how I wanted so much to come that Ma finally let me go. But I didn't tell what happened with the man on the beach. I was ashamed to say. I said I fell asleep on the beach and then the storm came and how I ran and fell and how my clothes got so wet and made me so cold I had to take them off.

She said, "I guess you got it on the jetty rocks," and I nodded. She said, "I guess you won't be sleeping on the beach no more." She said, "What kind of job you looking for?"

I hadn't thought about the job until then when she asked. Then I didn't want a job or the sea or the beach or any of the Island. I only thought of Ma and of going home and being with Jimmy and Pa and Amos and the rest.

I couldn't tell her about the job because my eyes began to tear and my throat burned so I couldn't speak.

She said, "Maybe you'd better rest today and see about a job tomorrow." She said, "On top of the ice box there's a tin with needles and thread to fix that shirt of yours." She said, "I gotta go now. If you're feeling better come on down to the office."

I nodded and she went off. That was the last

place I wanted to go, down to that office where I might see that man again. I lay my head down on the table and cried, and couldn't stop the crying.

I wanted Ma so bad. I wanted to call Mrs. Finney and have her tell Ma to tell Jimmy to come and get me. I didn't want to walk along that road no more or ride alone all that way back home.

My head was aching from the crying. I said, "Stop your squawkin'!" I said, "Stop your squawkin' and take yourself a shower!"

I could feel that sand caked against my scalp. There was sand between my toes and up my behind and in my ears and all over.

The shower ran fine and hot. I soaped my hair and my skin, soaping good to wash away all the dirtiness. I let the water run and run and my head got clearer under the running water. I scrubbed until my skin was sore, scrubbing until the blood ran up red to my skin and tingled.

There were nice thick towels hanging near the shower and they dried the water off real quick. At home our towels don't dry as good, just your arms and your back, and the towel is as wet as your body.

I stood and looked at myself in the mirror. My

eyes were puffy but my lips were not so full as they felt. Except for my eyes my face looked all right, not no scratches or bruises or nothing, but my neck had dark red splotches all around and I got sick to my stomach remembering. I wondered if the lady saw those marks and if she knew what they were and why she made me say I stumbled on the jetty.

There was a round box of powder on the shelf above the toilet. It had a big round puff and the powder smelled sweet and strong of flowers. I brushed the puff around my neck and the powder ran up my nose like dust and made me sneeze. The powder stayed white on my neck with the blotches showing through, brown against the white. I towelled the powder off my neck and took iodine from the chest and covered each splotch dark brown with iodine.

The phone rang and it was Brooklyn. She wanted to know how I felt and when I said "Better," she told me to come down and have a sandwich at the office which was also the bar and the restaurant. I said I wasn't hungry and she said my friend in number eight checked out early in the morning and then I said I'd be down as soon as I fixed my shirt and got dressed.

She was tending bar and waiting table when I came in. I had my shirt collar standing up and the front buttoned high all the way but still she said, "Jesus, what the hell did you do to yourself?"

I tried to shrink my head into my shoulders, but she said, "Never mind, go behind and get a bite to eat."

I went behind the bar but I didn't eat. I saw a pile of dishes in the sink and washed them and set them drying in the wire baskets. When the tables emptied she came behind and made two ham sandwiches and took two Cokes and we sat on the bar stools and ate.

She said, "Number eight must've got out early because he was gone when I got here." She said, "I got his licence number if you want to get him jailed." She said, "Of course that's not what I'm telling you to do. Might make it worse for you letting people know, but then that bastard should get punished, but then your name'd be mud."

I couldn't look up to see her face while she was doing all that talking.

She said, "What kind of a job you after?"

I said I wasn't sure. I said I wasn't sure I'd stay. I said I was thinking of going back home. I thought of Ma and the darned water came running to my eyes.

She said, "Foolish not to give it a try." She said, "What d'you want to crawl home for? It's not going to be any easier there."

I said, "I want to tell Ma. I want to tell Jimmy."

She said, "Some things is better not told. Some boy friends can't believe and can't trust no more."

"Jimmy's not a boy friend! He's my brother."

She said, "There's some things that shouldn't be told to family, even to a mother. There's some things a mother doesn't ever want to know."

I thought, Ma's not like that. Ma would know what to do, what to say to make it right again.

She said, "Go on out and take a walk and look around." She said, "Don't make up your mind too soon." She said, "Don't go 'way without saying goodbye. You owe me that. You owe me saying a goodbye."

I promised I wouldn't go without seeing her first and got out. When I slammed the door I noticed the printing that said owned by Stanley and Wilhelmina Haver. She was a real Wilhelmina. She was a regular Willie.

I walked not on the beach but on the black tar road. I looked at the little houses built near the road and the kids playing in the yards and the clothes hanging on the lines and the flowers and the leaves growing in the gardens. Walking on the road you could see the water and the sky and you couldn't tell where one ended and the other started. It was all running together, a blueness running together.

I saw the dock and walked out to the dock. The wood creaked under my feet. The slats were wide with spaces in between. I saw the boats pulling in and going out and the kids sitting at the edge with string lines hanging over and the men standing holding onto fancy rods.

The sun was shining warm and the water gently rippling and the wind was soft and cool. The dock was dry and the road was dry and the sand was dry. It was as if it had never rained, like it had never rained or stormed, like it had never been cold or dark or thundering. Now it was all calm and warm and it looked like peace and like it would always be calm and warm and never storm again.

I thought of the storm and the man and about what happened on the beach. I thought of Ma and how I'd say it and what she'd say. I didn't want Pa to know or Paul or Carolne or Edna or Mrs. Finney or any of the others, just Ma and Jimmy. I'd just tell Ma and Jimmy and I wondered what they'd say.

Jimmy'd be sore. Jimmy'd be good and sore and his feet would shuffle instead of spring and his eyes would pop like they do when he's really sore. Jimmy wouldn't be sore at me but at the man. Jimmy didn't like anyone to touch me. Jimmy didn't like anyone hitting me when I was little and played with the kids in the street. But Jimmy couldn't fight, not fight with hands and feet. Jimmy'd scream and holler till a vein stood out blue on his neck and his eyes got big and almost popped from out the lids.

There'd be no sense telling Jimmy. Jimmy would be awful hurt. Be so hurt all the rhythm would drain out and his arms would hang heavy at his sides and his legs shuffle instead of dance and Jimmy would not be Jimmy with the hurt.

Ma would be sore too. Ma would call that man all kinds of names and ask me questions in between. Ma would ask, "Why'd you take a ride?" Ma would say, "You had a five, why were you begging a ride?" Ma would say, "Why a man? Plenty women driving cars!" Ma would say, "Why'd you drink his Coke? Why'd you drink his beer?" Ma would say, "Why didn't you scream?" Ma would say, "I told you never trust a stranger. I told you not to go. I told you and told you and told you!" Then Ma would get riled at me and I would be the one she'd be sore at and I would be the one to get beat.

I never liked the names that Ma kept calling Caroline. It wasn't right to call her that and have the neighbors listen and the kids hear and repeat what they heard and call her that themselves. I know Caroline wasn't really a tramp or a slut or a bum or anything like that. Plenty of girls even in my class at Catholic school curled their hair and wore lipstick and went to parties and went with boys. I never went to a party but Jimmy says they put the light out and sit around in the dark kissing and being vulgar. And Caroline isn't just fifteen. Caroline's almost eighteen and almost graduated. Caroline said how'd she ever marry if she couldn't go with boys. Caroline said that all the girls go out in cars and get in after twelve.

I know Ma doesn't mean it when she calls those names. I know the kids don't mean it when they call Caroline that. They just do it to rile her and it does and they are not the words they get their mouths washed out for, so they can say them all they want.

I don't ever want anyone calling me bum or tramp, especially Ma. And Ma could say them now and it would be true and I'd feel awful bad not sore like Caroline.

Caroline said that it was worse for her because she's the first girl and she was paving the way for us and when we got older and started going out it would be easier. Ma would be used to things then and be a lot more modern.

Ma said she knew she'd never have to worry about me. Ma said it was good to have one sensible girl in the house. Ma said that maybe I should wear a little lipstick on Sunday and go to the church dances or to the roller skating at least.

I didn't like the feel of grease against my lips and wouldn't go to the dances or the skating. Even for Jimmy I wouldn't go. Jimmy'd take me. Jimmy always asked me if I wanted to go. All the kids knew Jimmy was my brother and they'd think he had to drag me along. And when Jimmy dances he forgets you're there and starts doing all kinds of crazy steps like when you're home and with all the people watching you get big and heavy and your legs don't move and Jimmy has to pull you around like you're a clump of lead.

The noise of everyone talking and laughing makes me nervous. Like Caroline said the noise of the kids playing and crying drives her nuts. That kind of noise doesn't bother me, I don't even hear it, even with all the kid's noise it is still and calm and peaceful.

It was peaceful on that dock. Everybody minding their own business, fishing or walking or just standing. And no one staring and I felt like I had been here before but I never had. I felt like this was the place for forgetting and dreaming and remembering, remembering only the good things.

It was a long while before I walked back to the Wailing Whale. I saw her walking up the gravel drive to the motels at the top of the hill. She was bending over like it was too much to keep her head up straight and her arms hung and the keys jangled in her hand.

"Where you been all this while?"

I said, "Down by the dock." I said how nice it was down there and how it made me feel and how I was going to stay and how I wasn't going to be a baby and run home because things didn't go so right.

She said, "Good!" She said, "I know some of the guys who own some of those fishing boats." She said, "How'd you like a job on one of them boats?"

"Sure!" I said, "Sure!" I was darned glad she didn't ask me to work for her, not that I wouldn't have liked working for her, but it would all be inside work and I might just as well be in the Bronx as out here in the open on the Island.

She said, "You can stay here with me in the cottage, except on weekends when my husband comes out. Then maybe you can sleep in the office or if we're slow in one of the empties." She said, "I'm no sucker and don't stand for no nonsense. You do your share or you go." She said, "Hey kid, what's your name?"

I told her, "Francine McGuire." I told her, "Everybody calls me Francie." I told her I'd pay to stay and I wouldn't be no nuisance.

She said her name was Wilhemina Haver though I already knew it. She said to call her Willie and I was glad because that's what I'd been calling her in my mind. She said her husband had this job in Brooklyn and couldn't come out except on week-ends. She said her husband was a carpenter and built the cabin and the office and the motels him-self. She said she did the designing and he did the building. She said next year or maybe the year after they were going to build a pool. She said she had it all drawn up and it would be in the shape of a whale and the water pouring in would come from a fountain and squirt up like you see in the pic-tures of a whale.

I didn't say it would be a waste what with the beach and the sea right there. Maybe people pay-ing twelve dollars a night needed a pool and a fountain squirting up. Maybe people paying twelve dollars a night needed the private beach though they might never go down to lie in the sand but only see the sign saying WAILING WHALE PRIVATE

BEACH and they feel like they're getting twelve bucks' worth. Maybe they'd never go near the pool or use the chairs or the umbrellas but they'd know it was there and feel good for the knowing and write home and tell all about it and make out like they were having a real swell time.

When Ma got picture postcards from the neighbors they all were having the swellest times. Sometimes you could see through the bright colors that the place was seedy but they always wrote how swell it was and how much they were eating, as if there was never any food in the Bronx.

Ma and Pa never went away. Pa on his vacation sat in McGinty's and took Ma to the show at night. Pa on his vacation went to the stores and bought himself some clothes.

Ma said, "No place is as good as home." Ma said, "It's useless to run for a week and then come back and have to live in the same old hole all over again." Ma said, "Couldn't stand to have people waiting on me and kissing my ass and hovering near. I wouldn't kiss nobody's ass and I don't expect nobody to be kissing mine." Ma said, "Someday when you kids are grown and married your Pa and I will take a real vacation. We'll take a real vacation and go to Ireland and stay in the old country for awhile. There it is cool and green, a real green green, not like here where everything dries up and dies so fast, and there are real small houses and when you look from the window everything is green and the sky and the clouds seem near and everything is slow and clean and green."

I know how Ma felt about the green. It was like I feel about the blue of the sea and the salt smell and the cool feel of water in the air. And I know how Willie and her husband must feel about the motel and the office and the cabin they both built, and the pool that they were going to build.

I didn't say nothing about not liking a pool shaped like a whale and I didn't say nothing about that Wailing Whale sign that blinked all night like McGinty's Saloon sign. Maybe McGinty's proud of that sign that shines in the windows and blinks on and off and don't let no one sleep.

Willie checked the empties to make sure they were clean and ready in case anyone drove up and wanted one. She looked in the bowls to make sure they were flushed and checked to see that the stoppers weren't left in the sinks and to be sure that the ashtrays were emptied. She said a woman named Sarah who lived nearby did up the rooms but she always checked to make sure things were right. Willie said that sometime in April someone left the stopper in the sink and the water running and had flooded the place. She said she lost the mattress and the spring and a month's rent from number five and there was nothing she could do to the slob that left the stopper in the sink.

She said, "Everybody thinks it's all pure gravy and so did I but now I know. It's no picnic. Having a motel is no great picnic."

We went back to the office and I met this girl Elsie who helped out waiting on table and tending bar. Elsie was about as old as Caroline and her folks owned a cottage near the beach and every summer they came out and lived there. Elsie went to college in the fall and in the summer she worked to get the money for the clothes she wore to school.

Elsie took the orders and Willie cooked and I washed the dishes. Willie said I didn't have to but I hated just sitting around. Then Elsie, Willie, and I had some chowder and fried fish and french fries and beer. Willie said if she were my mother she'd never let me be drinking beer. Willie doesn't look anywheres near as old as Ma.

Captain Powers came in and Willie spoke to him and Captain Powers said sure I could have the job. He said he could use another hand and asked if I ever worked a boat before. He said there was nothing to it and all I had to do was sell tickets and bait the lines and sell candy and soda to those that wanted.

The boat was supposed to pull out at nine-thirty in the morning but it usually left at a quarter to ten to make sure everyone who was coming was there. I had to be on board at eight and help swab the deck and get the bait cut up and sell the tickets. When the people came on board I gave out string lines to those who didn't come with rods. We had to help them climb aboard and some of the ladies were so scared you almost had to pull them down the ladder.

We had all kinds of people come aboard. Some who came to fish and some who came for the ride and some who'd never been on a boat before and hung sick on the rail and got everyone around them feeling pretty sick.

We had some days when the strikes were so

good the Captain could've stayed right at the dock and let them haul them in and other days when no matter where he went there was nothing and the people grumbled and they said he didn't know the good spots and said he was a lousy Captain and the boat was lousy and the bait rotten and scaring the fish away.

Sometimes the people got together and were friendly and made a pool for a prize for the biggest fish and sometimes no one talked to anyone and it was almost embarrassing when they had to call out loud for bait.

There was some that caught the fish like it was nothing and they didn't care, never saying a word or acting excited when they brought them in. And some got such a thrill the whole boat knew even if they only got a nibble.

Once we had this couple on the boat. They were married, and he had a rod and I gave her a drop line and she was all squeals about the bait even though it was only squid and mackerel and she didn't have to touch it. She got this here nibble and screamed loud and jumped and pushed her leather jacket off the rail into the water and her husband tried to grab the jacket and lost his rod. All her nibble was was a sea robin and I had to throw him back because they're not good to eat and we always threw them back. She squawked while we tried fishing for her jacket and his rod and got nothing but empty hooks.

Sometimes the water was calm, real calm and smooth and the boat hardly rocked at all. And sometimes it was choppy and after we were out a while it looked like it would storm and some were all for turning back and others had to have their money's worth even if they drowned.

Once we got caught in a storm and the boat rolled, it rained and thundered and most were sick with the rolling. The way the wind was blowing we couldn't head for the dock and some were scared and the Captain said to keep them fishing, to keep them eating candy if they could. I was feeling sick too but I didn't have no time to spend against the rail. I was running back and forth, too busy to be scared and some of the men made out like they were helping the Captain with the boat. We had one lady drop on her knees praying and crying out loud and some of the other ladies started to cry and scream and I got plenty scared. That lady stayed on her knees all the time of the storm screaming out to the Lord to save her and her husband and the other men couldn't drag her to her feet or stop her screaming. When the storm stopped so did her screaming and she stayed in the toilet till we docked and the boat was cleared. Her husband swore through the locked door that no one was left on deck. She wouldn't look at us or let anyone help her up the ladder. She wouldn't look at none of us but we looked at her, we kept looking until we couldn't look to see her walking down the dock no more.

There was some that spent three dollars to fish and gave their fish away. Lots of times I got their fish and brought it home to Willie. Willie wouldn't let me pay for board. Willie said to send some money home to Ma and save. Willie said it was important to have some money saved. I never spent the five that Pa had given me and I put it in the bank with all the rest.

Sometimes I would get up and go to the sea about five in the morning. It was cool and the tide was out and the sand and the stones were smooth and cool and moist and it felt like snow that no one ever walked on. It was like God was near on the beach and it felt like organ playing and Ave Maria and how you feel in church on Christmas Eve.

I'd fill my scarf and my pockets full with clams and drop them back at the cabin and leave a note for Willie telling about the clams, so she would know. Then I'd wash the scarf and walk down to the boat holding it out so that it was almost dry by the time I walked the dock. This scarf was red and a little green and yellow, a square of cotton like the farmers use to blow their nose. Willie gave it to me the first day I worked on the boat. She said, "Here wear this on your head to keep your hair from turning straw," but I knew she meant for me to cover my neck so no one would see. The scarf was with me all the time. I used it for carrying clams and fish and ice and berries, for hiding my neck and blowing my nose.

Sometimes after the boat pulled in I'd get a lift to the village and I would buy a strawberry pie or some fancy whipped cream cake and bring it back with me to the office and then when it was quiet Willie and me and Elsie would have a party filling up on pie or cake.

Willie always talked about going to the movies.

Willie said that when she was home in Brooklyn she went to the movies three times a week or more. She said sometimes she'd go straight from one movie to another. Then she'd say that she hadn't been to a movie since April and it was too bad she had to work so hard and couldn't take one night off to go to a show. Then I'd say she should go. I would say I'd stay and mind the place and she should go. But she would never go. She'd say why didn't I go. She said she didn't need me hanging around and I should go to the dances in the village or go around with Elsie and her friends or meet some kids my own age and get out more and be sociable. She pestered Elsie to take me out with her and introduce me to some boys, but I wouldn't go.

Willie and I stayed up late in the office and played gin rummy.

In a way Captain Powers was like Willie. Captain Powers came to the bar every night and sat around drinking beer and saying how he could go for a plate of spaghetti and how the smell and taste of fish was getting him sick. He said the first bad day when the boat couldn't go out he'd go to the Hamptons and eat a ton of spaghetti. He said he knew this Italian place that made spaghetti so good you could smell it a block away. He said their spaghetti was lasting, the taste stayed with you and everything you ate for the next week tasted like spaghetti.

Willie always argued that chow mein was better and Captain Powers always promised to take Willie to this place and show her which was better.

Even when the weather was bad Captain Powers never rode out to the Hamptons. All day he'd work on the boat and in the evening he came to the bar and forgot to talk about spaghetti.

It worked out fine sleeping at Willie's. There was only one room in the cottage and when Stan came in I couldn't stay. Those nights I slept on the boat. There were blankets on the boat and it wasn't cold. There was a hot plate and a pot for coffee so it was all right and I felt I was a baby, rocking. When it was too cold or it rained I stayed in one of the motel empties. There was always empties if the weather wasn't right.

Stan was a right nice guy. Always quiet, always sawing. You could tell he was a carpenter the way he always handled wood. I could tell when Stan was there by the sound of the drill or the pounding or the smell of the fresh sawed wood.

He belonged with Willie. She was always talking and he listening. Willie was always saying how good Stan was and how she wished someday I would meet a man as good as Stan. Willie said the first thing she liked about Stan was his name. She said she liked the name Haver because it had a clean sound and felt good on her lips and good in her ears. Willie said once she was going with this guy whose name was Emory Schlinghammer and couldn't get to like him because of his name. She said every time she said Wilhemina Schlinghammer her stomach turned sick. She said going through so many years of her life as Wilhemina Schwartz was bad enough.

I said that all kids should have the right to name themselves. I said I felt sorry for Torrence when he grew up and had to be called that, with the teachers calling him Torrence in school and the kids making fun. Pa and Caroline and Paul and I begged Ma not to name Torrence Torrence but she did anyway. I said how I hated the name Francine and how I made Jimmy call me Frankie when I was little but I never said nothing about calling Jimmy Geranium. I said I was surprised Willie's name was Schwartz. I said I never dreamed Willie's name was ever Schwartz.

Fat boys are Jews and old men with beards and long black coats and long skinny noses and long skinny witch-like women and dark fat round women, they are the Jews. Not Willie. Not Willie!

I never saw a cross on Willie's neck. I never saw blessed pictures on the walls. She never went to church but neither did I, there was no Sunday on the boat. I never never thought of Willie as a Jew. Never thought to think of Willie as a Jew.

She said, "Why?" Willie wanted to know why it was hard to believe her name was ever Schwartz.

I couldn't say. I couldn't say it was because Schwartz was a Jew's name. I couldn't say that I never thought Willie was a Jew. I said I never thought of Willie having any other name than Haver and that was why I was so surprised.

Willie never acted like a Jew, or Stan. Willie ate ham and bacon and everything. They never spoke the way Jews speak, or ate the way Jews eat.

I never dreamed Willie was a Jew. I ate with Willie and with Stan and we'd have french fries and cole slaw and fish or meat and rolls and butter and tomatoes and ice cream. Willie was no cheap skate and she filled the plates up full and it was all American, no matzo balls or gefilte fish or things like that. I never ate so much in all my life as I did with Willie and I was showing it. I never thought Willie was a Jew.

After, when I'd see the sign that said all those things like MOTEL, BREAKFAST, DINNER, COCKTAILS AND BEER, then for a minute I'd think Jews. But Willie needed to have a place to eat at the motel. Some people don't like to have to drive around looking for a place to eat, especially in the morning. The office and the bar and the restaurant was important. It was a place the wives could stay while the husbands went out fishing. It was a place the men could come back to after being out in the sun and the wind all day and sit and drink beer and talk to Willie and to Elsie and to me and to the others that came in to sit at the bar in the evening.

It was a place for Captain Powers and some of the other boat men to come for awhile and tell the things that needed telling.

It was never crowded. It wasn't a big place and it was never crowded or never rushed. There were only four tables and I never saw all of them taken at once.

Sometimes one of the guests came in and sat at the bar all day, that made Willie nervous. Willie wondered why they drove all the way out to the Point to sit at a bar. Some people rode in from Jersey or Pennsylvania and never went out fishing or to the beach, they just sat around drinking at the bar as if a shot of rye or a glass of beer tasted better if you paid twelve bucks a day to drink it.

Sometimes a wife would sit at a table waiting all day for her husband to come back from fishing. Sometimes they sat quiet and sometimes they got gabby and gabbed all day. Most of the time they were sore at being left alone so long and were pretty touchy. Once we had a lady who sat drinking martinis all afternoon and complaining about the martinis and the place. She said she was damned sorry she let her husband bring her to a place as dead as this Montauk was. She said she'd never been to a place that didn't have a movie or nothing. She said next time her husband wanted to fish he'd have to fish from Provincetown. She said there was a lot doing in Provincetown. She said that all the places in Provincetown had fairy waiters.

Willie said that the next year she was going to import some fairies right from Greenwich Village. And the woman was sure sorry that she came a year too soon.

I almost broke up. I had to crawl behind the bar and sit on the floor laughing. I almost split my skin laughing.

Willie said I'd be splitting my jeans, they were getting so tight. Pa wouldn't have nothing to say about me being skinny, scrawny. Pa wouldn't have said I was built like a boy if he saw me then. Elsie bought me a brassiere in town and it was hurting with the growing. Willie kept saying to stick my stomach in and I tried but I couldn't and I felt like I was ready to explode. Willie cut out the french fries and the ice cream and loaded me up on tomatoes and cole slaw.

I kept writing home and telling Ma how fat I got and when Jimmy wrote back he said they could never believe it. I said they'd all see. In two more weeks school would start and I'd be home. In two more weeks they'd see I wasn't skin and bones no more.

Every time I thought of going home I was glad to be seeing Ma and Jimmy and the rest and then I'd get sad at leaving the boat and the Point and Willie.

Willie said I had to come out and see her in Brooklyn. Willie said if I wanted I could come out to the point on weekends before the weather got bad and she closed up the motel for the winter. Willie said that one night before I went back we'd have to go out on a celebration. Willie said she'd leave Elsie and Sarah minding the place and we'd go out to East Hampton and have dinner out and shop for clothes and take in a show.

Willie said I needed clothes bad. She said I shouldn't wear jeans no more because my behind and my belly stuck out. I cut out drinking beer and soda and stuck to water but still I couldn't close my jeans but with a pin.

Willie said it wasn't too bad if the kids called you skinny but it was rough if they called you fat.

It was funny that my face or arms or legs didn't fill out. Willie said that maybe once you couldn't tell if I was boy or girl but now you'd have no trouble telling.

Willie asked me when I had my girl friend last

and I could not remember. I never watched the days all summer except the days I was off from the boat and that was not the same day every week. I knew the weekends were when Stan came out and I knew the summer was over and it was September from Jimmy's letter. I couldn't remember when I'd had my girl friend last. I knew I never had it here in Montauk and I never even missed it.

Willie said that when we were in East Hampton maybe we should stop in to see the doctor.

I said, "Why?"

It couldn't be what she was thinking. It couldn't be. Maybe it didn't come because I was away from home and working on a boat. Maybe getting hit by the waves all the time stopped it.

I said I was getting fat because I ate too much. I said I never ate so much in all my life. I never had ice cream every day or eggs and bacon and honey and pies and Pepsies. I said it was the air and the food and the not washing clothes and the not scrubbing floors that filled me out, nothing else.

Willie said she was sure it wasn't nothing and I shouldn't worry.

It made me sick and I ran down to the beach

and puked in the water. The waves carried it out and brought it back. Coming in and out like forgetting and remembering. I remembered the black and his face, not clear but parts, the wiry hair and the hair of his arms, of his chest and the sweat smelling from the hairs. I could hardly breathe with the remembering, my insides blowing up and squeezing out the air and pounding pounding in my ears.

Not crying or screaming like I did that night on the beach, and it didn't rain or storm, the skies stayed clear and the wind cool and even and the thunder didn't come with the remembering.

I lay on the beach and my chest hit the sand and they hurt and I knew why they hurt. I put my hands on my belly and felt the roundness, it used to be so flat, flat like a boy's it was and now it was round and hard and full.

It is a terrible shame to have a baby and not be married. It is a sin and God would take me for my sin and I lay on the beach waiting, waiting to be taken.

Part
Three

*T*he WAILING WHALE winked out and it was weird and black, dark black and still, except for the wind whistling. Only the wind and the water rushing and I could hear myself breathing against the sounds of the screaming wind.

The sun made pale streaks in the winter's wind.

The light burned in the ceiling but the black crept up and crawled in shadows on the walls. My eyes burned from the reading, from the watching, and closed from the burning until the wind screamed and the lids pulled open. I stayed waiting, listening until ears closed with the listening and I dozed between the wails of the wind.

In the calm dawn, when the light chased the black from staring in the windows, I shut the light and slept for rest.

Willie said it would be lonely here with the motel closed and no one coming. Willie said not to stay alone but to go with her to Brooklyn.

I couldn't go and let them stare.

Willie said no one would know. Willie said to wear a ring and say my husband was in service. But I would know and I would feel them stare and I would know the lie.

I didn't know what to write and tell to Ma. I couldn't go back to Ma and back to school. Ma would be ashamed, and Caroline. I hate a lie and I had to lie. I had to make up a lie till it sounded true but nothing sounds true in a lie.

In a letter, I wrote and said I had an all year job. I said I was going to school in Montauk and it was a good school and the nuns were nicer than the ones in the school in the Bronx. I said I was going to work after school but I wouldn't make much so

I wouldn't be sending much home. I said that I missed them all and I would try to come home and see them all at Christmas, even though I knew I wouldn't.

The letter took me days to write and days to mail. I mailed it in September when Jimmy wrote asking what was wrong and why I was not home in time for school. I thought of trying to see Jimmy and telling him the truth, but then Jimmy'd have to lie and Jimmy would be hurt and there was no sense hurting Jimmy.

They knew the lie. I came in swinging fish and saw Pa sitting at the bar. He didn't look comfortable like he did at McGinty's. I had nothing to say but hello and then it was quiet. Pa didn't say much except everything at home was fine. Ma was fine and Caroline and Torrence and all the rest and Jimmy was bringing home a good pay and working after school and all day Saturdays at the butcher's. Paul was doing fine and liking it in the army and Edna had my Saturday night baby sitting job and was rolling cigars after school and Caroline was getting ready to graduate. I wondered who took over the floors and the washing but Pa wouldn't know. Pa was quiet and Willie fixed a couple of plates even though Pa said he wasn't hungry. Pa was quiet and Willie tried to make some talk by telling about the hurricane and Pa said he ought to go before he got caught in it. Pa said goodbye and I would have died if he said skinny, scrawny, but he didn't.

Willie said Stan talked to Pa before I came in and told him how things were. Willie said Stan had to tell because Pa came in mad and started accusing them of using me for a maid and he said he was taking me back with him right away. Willie said Stan talked to Pa and Pa said I could stay.

It made it easier thinking about the hurricane, but the hurricane was only a good rain and a strong wind.

Jimmy sent a package and a letter. Jimmy sent my winter coat and my St. Agnes jumper and my blouse and my shoes and underwear. Jimmy sent his last term's school books and a new box of stationery with roses printed on the corner. Jimmy said that everyone at home was fine and that he was glad I was fine and that they all missed me and was sorry I had not come home this fall. Jimmy said he wanted to come out instead of Pa but Ma wouldn't let him. Jimmy said that the first chance he got he'd come out to see me. He said he didn't know when that would be because there was so little time with working after school and Saturdays and all the homework that the third year got. Jimmy said to read the books he sent and study so that I could make up what I missed when I went back to school. He said he hoped I stayed well and if there was anything I needed, to write and tell him. He said to write often but not to send my letters home. Jimmy said the new box of paper was so I shouldn't forget to write and when I did to send it to him in care of Dewey the butcher.

I cried. I knew Ma wasn't wanting a tramp for a daughter. It was as if Ma and Pa and all the rest had died and I would never see them all again. In the black nights I took the letter out and read it in the light. Then I'd forget the wind and the dark and the aloneness with all the feeling bad.

It was to feel bad when the iceman came, or when I shopped for food in town, or when Sarah stopped by to visit and sat in the chair and stared as my stomach grew bigger. Only Captain Powers never said nothing about why I never left for school though all the rest did and there was no one but me to help on the boat after September.

The boat was not crowded like it was in July or August and sometimes there was nobody so the boat didn't go out and sometimes Captain Powers took me out for a ride, not a fishing ride, but all the way out. Sometimes we'd go around the sound and see Connecticut and sometimes we rode out and sailed the ocean.

It was good to sit and watch the waves and eat my lunch and dream. It is to dream with the rocking. I knew why Uncle Louie went to sea though Ma could never know the reason why. Uncle Louie died in the war at sea. Ma grieved for Uncle Louie, but I know Uncle Louie wasn't scared of dying in the sea. That lady was, the one they couldn't pull from kneeling on the deck, the one that cried loud praying to the Lord. I wonder if she'd scare so riding in a car. I knew that number eight in his bright green Ford wouldn't be afraid to die in a car, and I knew Captain Powers wouldn't scare of dying in the sea. And maybe Ma would be at peace if she died on the green green grass of Ireland and Jimmy while his feet were tapping and a bunch of people clapping and Willie—I couldn't ever think of Willie dying.

When the boats stopped going out, the motels closed. The Wailing Whale shut down and Willie went on back to Brooklyn. Then there was nothing to do but walk and read and dream.

When the wind died and the sun softened the sting of the cold I'd walk to town and buy some things I'd need, things different from the cans and boxes Willie stored for me. I would walk up the beach and try a line in the water off the dock. The wind was strong on the water but it was good when the fish pulled in. It was good to have the taste of real fresh fish on my tongue again.

If the sun was weak and the cold burned your breath back in your throat I stayed in and read. I'd sit by the window to save the light for burning through the night and read Jimmy's books or the letters Willie sent.

Willie sent letters and packages. Willie sent things she bought and things she made. Willie knitted little sweaters and bootees and scarves and things, all in fancy stitches with ribbons and bows and fuzzy white angora trimmings. Before Stan left he made a cradle, a small white rocking cradle and Willie painted little flowers on the white. Willie didn't mention the baby in the letters. She was wanting to know how I was and was worrying about me being alone out here. Willie told all about what she was doing in Brooklyn, about where she went and what she did. Willie didn't say nothing about the baby though I knew what she was wanting to say and I was waiting for the letter to come right out and say it.

Willie never had a baby. That night that we went to town and to the doctor's and saw the show and ate in the Italian place that Captain Powers always spoke of, Willie told me how she could never have a baby. It was after the doctor's, and Willie was eating spaghetti and I was eating Jello because my throat was so tight I could not swallow.

The doctor was not as old as he should have been and I was embarrassed because he was not so old. He had fancy leather chairs in the waiting room and Willie stayed out there when he called me in. He asked me all kinds of questions. He asked my name and my age and where I lived and what I was doing on the Island and what my symptoms were. I said I was feeling fine but was getting kind of fat. The doctor put me on a scale and checked my height and said I was not so over-weight and the fat would redistribute as I grew. He said I was a healthy looking girl. It was quiet. He sat waiting for me to go and I sat waiting for him to guess why I was there. He cleared his throat and I told him and then I was sorry I did.

The doctor said it would not hurt but I would not let him. The doctor said he could also tell by rabbits and that was fine. Let the rabbit, on that long white table, not I, not I.

The doctor said there were places to go that would take me in and take the baby. The doctor said I was too young and I should give it away and start my life all over.

There was nothing to start over. Maybe the doctor could with new leather furniture, or Willie with a motel, forgetting about babies with the motel and drawing pictures of a pool like a squirt-ing whale. There was no starting over for me. I could remember things from almost the day I was born, some bad things I'd like not to remember but they keep coming back with things that make for remembering.

I would not go to a place for girls like that. I would not go and have to eat what they felt like serving and have to sleep when they felt like shutting off the light. I wasn't going to sit and answer a lot of stupid questions. I knew about charity and knew about schoolteachery-looking social workers. I knew the way they came and told Ma what to buy and what to spend and Ma had to be nice and speak pleasant until they were out the door and she could say the things that needed saying.

I never said nothing to Willie about March and giving away the baby. Willie was knitting too much and buying too much. Willie sent me books on babies and vitamin pills and kept saying to eat well and drink milk and go to see the doctor. Willie said if I wasn't coming to Brooklyn she'd come out in March. All of March, she said, she'd come and stay. She'd stay from March to April and in April we'd be open like she planned. But Willie said nothing about what I was going to do when the baby came. Willie said nothing but I knew it was plenty on her mind.

Willie was swell like a mother. Willie was warm like a mother. Willie had no brothers or sisters. Willie had no one but Stan.

Willie said she had nothing to do in Brooklyn but get dressed up and go to the show and shop. Willie said that sometimes she'd spend a day just going from store to store never buying nothing just to kill a day. Willie said she knew women that bought things just so they could go back and return them.

Willie said that when Stan came home at night it was different. She didn't need to go out when Stan was there. Willie said when she first came out to Montauk she didn't think she could stay by herself. Willie said she couldn't stand to stay alone in her apartment in Brooklyn, but here she was so busy she didn't mind. She said she never got the blues at Montauk, she missed Stan the middle of the week but never got the blues. She said she especially liked this summer because I was there. Willie said she was glad we had met and got on so well and I said I was too.

I was glad for meeting Willie. Willie never took one cent from me all the time I stayed with her. I didn't have to pay to live all winter in the cabin and the cupboards and the office was filled with boxes and cans of food Willie bought to last me through the winter. Willie left cases of canned milk and canned meat and canned fish and canned fruits and canned vegetables and boxes of cereals and macaroni and rice and sacks of flour and potatoes and onions. Willie had a drawer filled with warm nighties and sweaters and long wool scarves and she said I could borrow whatever I felt like.

I borrowed, but I knew I borrowed and kept them washed clean and pressed so if Willie came and wanted to wear any of those things she could take it right out and it would be fresh like it was never borrowed. At home Caroline made you wash everything you borrowed even though it was not just fresh washed when you borrowed it. And she wouldn't ever lend to Edna because Edna always left stains and holes that weren't there before.

Willie was right, it was awful lonely here in winter, but I didn't mind the quiet of the days. I took to baking bread and cake in the days that I couldn't stay much outside and the house was warm with the oven going and the good smell of the baking lingered in the house all day.

The warmth and the smell of the baking was right for dreaming and I dreamed of things that were and things that were yet to be.

When it was warm enough for walking through the sand, I went to the beach and watched the water roll. I stood curling my toes in the sand and saw the rusted tins and the log and that wooden box which was no longer a box but sticks splintered in the sand. Someday I would take a basket and clear the rusted tins away. I'd leave the beach new and clean with nothing left to start the remembering. Only I had something else to keep me remembering. I had a thing, a growing thing to keep the remembering always growing.

I sat on the beach and the sand went up my skirt and I could feel the grains of sand against my legs, against my hands. It was cool clean sand and I thought of how the sand could go up between my legs and how it could rub and grow like it did in an oyster. I remembered that night and all the sand. I remembered how my scalp was caked with sand and how it was in my ears and in my mouth and eyes and up between my legs.

I thought of the oyster and the pearl and I

felt I was like the oyster that was growing a pearl, a great clean white round pearl.

There is nothing vulgar in the sea. There is nothing vulgar in a pearl growing in an oyster. I was like the sea, calm with the sea, pounding with the sea. Skin brown and battered with the wind. I would be as the sea. I would be the oyster of the sea and grow a pearl. I would have a pearl that grew round and hard inside of me.

Not to leave the sea. Stay with the wind and the cold and the snow by the sea. Clean by the sea, safe by the sea. Safe by the sea until the dark closed in and covered the sea and I was a tiny oyster huddled in the cabin with a burning light to keep the dark away.

In November the snow came and I let the water run to keep the pipes from freezing. The snow was white on the beach, white in the air, except for the tires on the road, untouched snow. All that clean white snow never to be touched. Back home in the Bronx, even in the early morning the snow had footprints on the sidewalk and slushy dirty tracks from the cars and the buses in the gutter. On the sills the snow was white and clean until the kids woke and grabbed at the snow before they had a chance to get outside.

Shovels scraped against the streets as snow turned into piles in the gutter. And the snow slithered back on the sidewalk as the kids jumped the piles and fought a war with snow.

At home in the Bronx, we have a high hill. A hill so high the cars strain and the wheels screech to make the hill. The people walking up bend forwards and those walking down arch their backs to keep walking with the hill. In the snow it was kids' hill, the cars couldn't climb or the people, just the kids and their sleds and flattened cardboard boxes that slid down almost as good as the ones with wood slats and metal runners. It took five times as long to get to the top as it did to slide to the bottom.

I remember when that hill was cleared of kids. Two kids bellywhopped and a red and yellow bus came and whopped their bellies. Jimmy said he'd never bellywhop again and the mothers kept their kids off the hill in the snow. After a time the mothers turned their heads away and it was kids' hill all over again. Jimmy never went down that hill again or I or Edna. We were too big to ever forget, but Peter and Timothy and Amos do, they do not remember. They never saw no kids squashed and they don't want to know when you tell them.

In November when the first snow came and settled on the ground, I thought of the boys and the hill and I got a twist inside my stomach. I thought of all the kids that came from all the blocks with their sleds to the hill and there are only three of ours to all of them. With all those kids it wouldn't be Peter or Amos or Timothy, but I remembered Jimmy and how it was almost he that got it under the bus and I stopped myself from thinking about that hill and the snow that falls in the Bronx.

Around Thanksgiving the snow came up and covered the windows and it was dark day and night. For two days the lines were down and there were no lights and no heat and no phoning in or out. Lucky there was the fireplace and wood and candles. I didn't use the candles except for reading. I kept pots of water boiling on the fire and put the pots around the room to keep it warm. I drank hot milk and hot soup and melted chocolate down in boiling water for a hot sweet drink. I was scared, so scared I'd sit and read the same line over and over, and I wouldn't cook nothing I had to chew, I couldn't chew nothing, and I couldn't do nothing but watch the fire or the windows and the candle flickering.

When I slept I had to leave the fire burn itself out. I used every blanket and Willie's flannel nightgowns and sweaters and pushed the bed over near the fireplace. When I woke it was cold and the water in the pots was cold as snow.

Thanksgiving Day I cried and thought of Ma and Pa and all the rest at home. I thought of the pictures of turkeys in the magazines. The fancy colored pictures with the turkey and all the trimmings fixed so pretty it would be a shame to dig in and disturb it all. At home Pa didn't like turkey so Ma made a ham or corned beef and cabbage and sweet potatoes and peas and small white onions and Pa would bring home soda and Jimmy and Caroline and Paul and I would bring home sweets. Once we all made up we'd bring home pies, all different kinds, and we had four kinds of pie to choose from. We'd get the little kids fed first and then we'd sit down all together and Pa would sit at the head of the table and dish the food onto plates and pass the plates around.

Once Pa took all of us who could walk and could sit quiet at a table to the Automat for dinner. That was before Paul was in service and there was Ma and Pa and Paul and Jimmy and me and Edna and Amos. We had to choose to see who would stay home and mind the rest. Edna lost and she felt bad, but Caroline said she would stay and take Edna's place. Edna thought it swell of Caroline to trade with her, but I think Caroline was ashamed to go even though the little ones would not be there. Maybe to Caroline, Edna and Amos were too little. Caroline never liked to come when we all went out somewheres.

Ma liked it eating out. Ma said it was quieter in that big place with all the people than it was at home with all the kids. Pa said we could choose whatever we liked and I had turkey and sweet potatoes and baked beans. Jimmy had frankfurters and fried potatoes and spaghetti even though it was Thanksgiving. The turkey was good but I could not eat it all. I could not get at all the meat with my knife and fork and I was ashamed to pick it up in my fingers even though Ma was and sucking on the bones.

I got hungry in the cold thinking about the food. I sat hungry thinking of food and about spending the rest of my life under snow.

The phone rang. It rang so loud I jumped and held my ears and stood still like I never heard a phone ring before. It was Sarah and she said the power was on. She said she had had it bad and her rheumatism was sore with the cold. She said the snow shovel crew was out and they just got through digging her place out and she was sending them up to me and if I wanted she'd send her husband up to get me and I could spend the night with her.

First I said yes, I was so glad to hear her and then I said no. I said there was too much straightening to do now that the power was on. I didn't want to go and hear about the storm and how she suffered and about her rheumatism.

I put on the lights and the heat and the stove and the radio. If there was someone near to phone I would have phoned them. The snow shovels were coming and it felt like a party. I put coffee on and hurried back and forth doing nothing, wondering if there was time enough to bake some bread or rolls before they came. There was only a little chocolate left to put on a plate.

The men came and made a path to the road and shoveled the drifts from the windows and drank the coffee. When they left I followed down the path to the road, though the sun was down it was light with the white all around. I watched the snow plow and the men in the truck with their shovels, and the plow pushed the snow in piles and the piles were almost as high as I. The sky was high and huge with pink streaks covering the blue. It was good to feel the air and see outside. I couldn't see the beach for the snow or see the water but I could hear the water lapping and the motors of the truck and the plow and it felt good with all the sounds.

Though it was late I was not tired and baked bread and cookies so I could put them in jars and never be out of sweets again. I washed my head and took a shower so hot my skin was red from scalding and washed clothes and the soot from the fire off the floor. I went to bed really tired, good and tired, with the room warm and smelling good from the baking. Sleeping without the light burning in the ceiling, and there was no dark creeping in but a brightness from the snow and the stars and the moon and I slept good without needing a light burning in the ceiling.

Near Christmas the radio played Christmas songs till I was tired of hearing them and the mail came with Christmas cards. There was a funny one from Willie and Stan, and one from Elsie and I was surprised she remembered me from the summer, there was a laughing Santa from Jimmy and one with a house and trees from Caroline, and a picture of the Blessed Mother from Edna and Amos. I almost wished they hadn't sent the cards so I wouldn't have to remember. I strung the cards up and hung them in the window and placed a large red candle on the sill.

There were real pine trees covered with snow for Christmas. No tinsel or colored balls or people hurrying, carrying boxes and boxes. No whispering and giggling and hiding presents and finding hidden presents and wrapping things with colored ribbon and buying. It is hard to buy for twelve and hard to hide for twelve. Once I carried a book every day to school and kept it out with my other books so Ma couldn't tell. It was a pretty book of flowers and no one saw the book and no one told and it was a real surprise for Ma and Ma almost liked it best, but Jimmy bought a bracelet with bright green stones.

We strung the tree with popcorn and the kids nibbled the popcorn until the tree was strung with string. The little ones ripped the wrappings and tore the ribbons, they ran for the brightest colors, the biggest boxes, they could not read.

In the quiet of the night before, with the tree trimming and the pea shelling and potato peeling we gave our gifts. Mrs. Finney brought in sweet burnt fudge and watched while we gave our gifts.

In the cottage there was no tree, only the wood walls and the carols coming from the radio and the string of cards hanging in the window. Real pines growing all around. I could of had a tree. I could of had a branch sticking in a jar. but I didn't. It is not right to have a tree here at Willie's. Jews do not have trees, and I would not have a tree at Willie's.

I made fancy cookies, some iced red and green and sent a box to Willie and saved a box for Sarah. Sarah might of phoned asking me to Christmas dinner.

Sarah phoned. She called to say she heard a man had come to town and was asking where I was and how to get on out to see me.

I kept the radio low and listened for his step. I locked the door and the windows and hid behind the curtain watching. I thought of calling Sarah and telling her to come on out to stay with me, or come on out and get me and let me stay with her, but then I'd have no reason and I couldn't tell about the man with the black hair running down his arms.

I couldn't think of no one else but him and I thought he had come to do the same thing all over again. It was a long time from that night but I remembered him clear. The pearl inside was round and large and my belly stretched round over it. The pearl turned and pushed against my insides and made the tight skin quiver. It pulled around and pushed hurting and lay quiet, still, hiding while I hid behind the curtain, waiting.

Like the thunder was the motor sound, but I wasn't watching thunder, I was lying quiet on the floor near the window hearing thunder break against the door. Breaking on the door, breaking back against my head though I was quiet, still. There was the noise all around, thundering on the window, thundering on the door.

The door was a plain wood door and the wood creaked and the door shook and the house shook. I lay shaking not looking, thinking to pull the bed against the door. But nothing moved except the door and the door moved back and forth, back and forth.

I heard the windows shaking in their wood and hoped the glass would break and cut me into pieces.

Through the thunder I heard the calling, name calling. I would not hear the name calling. I held my ears and would not hear.

I never heard my name before in thunder.

Never seen it wrote in lightning on the sky. There was no lightning, there was no sky, only the floor and I, covering ears and hearing the crying name through the pushed open door.

I would not hear. I would not see. My hands tight around my head, my knees pushed up and pressing on the pearl. I was a beggar in a rolling ball, rolling, rolling on the floor. Blind, deaf beggar, rolling.

There was no praying only saying, saying beggar's words.

The hands were shaking just like I. The voice was shaking too and kind of crying.

The hands were not man's hands with hard man's fingers, pulling. The hands were not man's hands at all. They were shaking patting hands that stopped the begging words, stopped the thunder sound so I could hear the crying calling.

The man was not so large and hairy. The man was not a man at all but my brother Jimmy.

Jimmy crying Frankie Frankie over and over while I was on the floor saying Jimmy. Jimmy had boxes in his lap and all around him on the floor and he could hardly hold me for the boxes.

Jimmy was wanting to know why I was hiding so scared on the floor and why I didn't answer when he called.

I said I was just silly scared because no one ever came and I wasn't expecting no one to ever come.

Jimmy said he knew he was going to come for a long time but he wanted to surprise me. Jimmy said it was the milk truck finally got him here and all the boxes had things in them for me. I opened the box of fancy cookies I was saving for Sarah and Jimmy made me open his boxes right away. There was a sweater from Caroline and a slip from Edna and a handkerchief with my name on it from Amos, not quite my name, it was Frances and that's pretty close. Jimmy gave me this great big silver paper box lined with blue velvet and filled with toilet water and dusting powder and rouge and lipstick. Caroline would go crazy to get a box like that.

I was sorry I had no present for Jimmy. I had nothing special for him to eat besides the fancy cookies. Jimmy said he was cold from the trip and did I have anything stronger than coffee. In the office I put five dollars under the clip in the register and took a bottle of whiskey. Jimmy poured and drank until the color came up to his face and his hands unloosed and his fingers tapped on the table.

Jimmy couldn't see why I stayed out here in Montauk with it being so cold and quiet. At first Jimmy wouldn't let his eyes come down from my face. He said he'd never thought my skin would brown and he was surprised to see my hair had grown. Afterwards he glanced down and saw my middle and his face twitched.

We had fishcakes and spaghetti and Jimmy got restless and walked up and down, and kept filling his glass with whiskey. Jimmy said he couldn't understand how I could stay in a one-room house. I told Jimmy how I was snowed in for two days without electricity and Jimmy said he would have gone real crazy.

Jimmy said he was going crazy now with the quiet and he turned the radio all the way up till you couldn't hear the sound, it was so loud. Jimmy wanted to know how to get to the village and I said "Walk!" Jimmy said he didn't want me walking so far and I said I always walked it and he said it was too cold, too long for me to walk.

We bundled warm. Jimmy wore Willie's sweater and Willie's scarf and waited down the road for a lift. I never took a lift from strangers ever since I came to Montauk but with Jimmy it was different. Jimmy danced with the cold on the road and drank up straight from the bottle. A laundry truck came by and I got up front and Jimmy got in back with the bundles and we got to the village without walking.

It was after dark and the drug store and the Post Office and the stores were closed except for the bar. We sat in a booth and Jimmy drank rye and soda and I had one beer and we talked.

Jimmy kept saying how it would be when I came back. Jimmy said that Caroline said that as soon as she graduated and was working steady she'd move to downtown Manhattan. Jimmy said as soon as Caroline moved he would too and they would both share expenses. Jimmy said he had money saved and he was going to quit his job and school too even though he only had a half year more to go. Jimmy said he was going to try and get a dancing part in a musical show. Jimmy said Caroline and he both wanted me to come with them. Jimmy said I could go to school in Manhattan and I wouldn't have to work unless I wanted. He said Caroline was leaving because she couldn't stand all the kids and the noise and the new rules and Jimmy didn't know if she'd like the idea if I brought a kid along.

Jimmy said there was new rules at home. Caroline was not allowed to wear lipstick or go with boys any more. Jimmy said Caroline and Edna were not allowed to be out after nine o'clock except if they were baby sitting and Caroline was sore because Timothy and Amos and Peter who were much younger stayed out late and Ma never said nothing to them.

I said I didn't think Caroline would want me to come along because the new rules were my fault. Jimmy said she did want me and if she didn't she wouldn't have sent the sweater. Jimmy said Caroline was planning to leave anyway and I said I knew she wanted to leave because she told me way back before I left for Montauk but I wasn't sure she would. Jimmy said he was sure of it now, Ma was getting big again and weaning Torrence.

Jimmy was as mad as Caroline ever was about Ma getting big. Jimmy said he hated Pa for making Ma always pregnant. Jimmy said he hated Pa and banged the table with his fists and cried. Jimmy said it was disgusting. Over and over, he said it was disgusting while he cried. Then he stopped and was quiet and drank some more.

I said I was thinking of giving the baby to Ma but now I couldn't with Ma having another. Jimmy laughed, he didn't say why he laughed but I knew he laughed because Ma wouldn't take the baby just as she wouldn't take me back.

Jimmy said I should put it in a basket and leave it in a Catholic church.

I said I wouldn't. I wouldn't ever do that. I said, didn't he remember the Home and the nuns and all those kids with the same color pajamas and the rows of beds and the tables with the lines of kids eating together, and the running noses and the snot-stained clothes. And waiting on Sunday for Ma and Pa to visit and when they didn't come how we felt with the other kids being called out for their visitors while we stayed in waiting. And when Ma and Pa came they stayed in the big room with the folding chairs all around the room with all the other visitors while the nuns watched to see they didn't steal their own kids away. And Paul crying, Paul and Caroline and Jimmy and I begging Pa and Ma to take us home, and Ma said tomorrow and I prayed all night like the nuns said to pray, praying all night for going home tomorrow and we didn't. We didn't go home until Paul ran away and Pa came and Paul and Caroline cried and begged and promised Pa they'd help Ma. Paul made Pa get Jimmy and me out too and it was like Christmas to be going home.

Ma pretending that the Home was like a boarding school rich kids went to. A rich kid wouldn't have to walk barefoot in the snow if some kid stole his shoes. Paul did. We were scared to go back and we helped so much because we were scared to go back. Jimmy and I were too young for school but we helped Ma with Edna and Timothy and Amos so we wouldn't have to go back to the charity home.

Jimmy said he didn't remember. Jimmy said if it was so, it was Pa's fault. Jimmy said Pa shouldn't have kids he couldn't afford to support. Jimmy said he couldn't remember and if it was so it was something Ma couldn't help because it was Pa's fault.

I said, "Ask Caroline!" I said, "Write and ask Paul!" I said, "Paul and Caroline and I won't ever forget. You don't want to remember that's why you let yourself forget." I said, "Ma didn't get us out, Pa did!" I said, "I won't ever stick my pearl in a charity home. I won't ever let the nuns get her to stick in a charity home."

Jimmy said it wasn't Ma's fault. Jimmy said if it wasn't for Pa and having to work in the butcher's he'd never leave Ma. Jimmy said Ma was old-fashioned and there was some things Ma didn't understand.

I said, "Is it old-fashionedness that made Ma forget me so quick?"

Jimmy said that wasn't true. Jimmy said it pained Ma so they weren't allowed to say my name at home.

I said Ma was thinking more about what the neighbors would say than about me.

Jimmy said that was a big lie. Jimmy said Ma was thinking about the rest of the family and what effect it would have on them. Jimmy said Ma didn't want Caroline or Edna to get any wrong ideas. Jimmy said Ma was afraid the whole family would lose their respect and that's why Ma didn't want me home, not that Ma forgot me or didn't care.

Jimmy drank some more. Jimmy drank as if he were used to drinking. I never saw Jimmy drink before except beer at home at the table, never before at a bar like Pa.

Jimmy said I could have gotten married and then come home. Jimmy said Ma wouldn't care if I was married. Jimmy said it would have been easy to make him marry me because I was under age and the guy could go to jail.

I said I couldn't marry him ever. I couldn't even think of him without feeling sick no less being married to him.

Jimmy said, why'd I do it then and he banged on the table like he did when he said he hated Pa. Jimmy said, why'd I do such a disgusting thing with someone I didn't like enough to marry. Jimmy said he never thought I'd do anything like that. Jimmy said I hurt him terrible. Jimmy said I hurt Ma and I hurt him, and he didn't believe Pa when he told it. Jimmy said that's why he had to come out for himself and see if it was really true. Jimmy said he hated Pa when Pa said that because he thought Pa was lying, and I was just sick or something, but now he knew that Pa wasn't lying. And Pa had said I was living with Jews. Jimmy said I could've spared Ma that. I could've spared Ma the living with Jews.

Jimmy banged the table and cried and the bartender came back and said maybe we had better go. Jimmy didn't want to leave but I said I wasn't feeling well so Jimmy felt he had to get me home.

When we got outside Jimmy said he was sorry. I tried to tell him what really happened but I didn't know how. I tried to tell him it wasn't really bad, that it was like being an oyster and growing a pearl, but Jimmy didn't understand. He thought I meant the name Pearl and he kept saying it was too common and I should name it Sapphire or Opal. Then he remembered Geranium and he said I should name it that. He said it was a beautiful name and a beautiful flower and Jimmy said I must call him that again.

It was cold and Jimmy wouldn't walk if I didn't call him that. It was a long way to the cottage and the road was dark. Jimmy took the flashlight and ran and danced up ahead and I had to follow running to keep up with the light. Once Jimmy lay down in the road and wouldn't move and I almost had to lift him and keep calling him Geranium before he'd stand again. It was cold but I wasn't thinking of the cold with worrying about getting Jimmy home. And Jimmy wasn't feeling much of the cold with all the drinking.

I got Jimmy to the cottage on a lie. I got Jimmy to the cottage by telling Jimmy I had another bottle stored away. Jimmy emptied all the drawers looking for the bottle. Jimmy found Willie's nightgown and put it on over his clothes. I tried to get Jimmy to drink coffee and eat some bread but Jimmy wouldn't take none unless I fed him with a spoon. Jimmy kept calling me Ma and kept saying I looked like Ma with my hair growing out and my stomach full. Jimmy stayed quiet while I dunked the bread in coffee and shoved it in his mouth with a spoon. Jimmy drummed his fingers on the table and on the silvery box while he called me Ma and sucked the soggy bread from the spoon. Then Jimmy took the cover off the box and stroked the inside velvet, stroking the soft blue velvet until he got tired of eating from a spoon and stroking the velvet and calling me Ma.

Jimmy played with the toilet water, smearing it on his arms and his face and neck. Jimmy said as long as his name was Geranium he'd have to smell as sweet as one. He put the bottle of the stuff to his lips and drank some and his face got white and his eyes popped till he vomited on the table and the floor and all over Willie's nightgown.

Jimmy cried and said he was sorry. He cried and said he hated himself and he hated everyone else. He hated being a butcher and the money he made and the money he gave to Ma and the free bacon Ma ate on Sunday mornings. He said we were all bad and it wasn't only me who was bad, it was the whole family. He said it must be something in our blood that made us bad. He said he was bad for drinking and Timothy was bad for stealing. He said Amos was bad because he caught Amos playing with himself, and Paul was bad because he had done bad things with bad girls. And Jimmy said he was worst of all because he was thinking of quitting his job and that would take the money from Ma and the bacon from her table. Jimmy said he was worst because he was bad so many ways. Bad as I, he was, and he knew how it was I felt when I went and did the thing I did. Jimmy told how the fellers horsed around, and I remembered how they horsed around, jumping one another, lifting, pushing, shoving, laughing hard, sitting on the newsstand, standing on the corner. Jimmy said, one night it was he who got it and they pulled him down and jumped on top. Jimmy said they got the buckle of his pants open and the belt off and the zipper unzipped and his pants pulled down, then they left off. Jimmy said he hollered and fought and tried hard to keep his pants up, but when they left off he was sick inside. Jimmy said he wasn't sick from the fighting or the roughness or from the pants off, but sick inside from the making believe, from the shame of his wanting them to finish whatever it was that they had started.

Jimmy kept saying he was sorry that he was like he was and I cleaned him up and he went to sleep, twitching and jerking all over the bed.

In the morning, with the knocking, Sarah came and saw Jimmy sleeping on the bed and said it wasn't right what I was doing. She said I had no right bringing men to Willie's place and carrying on behind her back while Willie trusted me. She said I was no good and she knew I was never any good from the first time she saw me even though I seemed so quiet. She said she could tell a bad one when she saw one and I was sure bad because I wore a man's shirt and man's jeans.

I tried to say in between her accusing that Jimmy was my brother, but she would not believe. She said to tell it to Sweeney and Jimmy woke and Sarah called him names and Jimmy swore and his eyes popped and he called her an f—ing busybody. Sarah swore she'd write to Willie and tell her what I was and how I was carrying on behind her back even while I was pregnant with a bastard.

Jimmy screamed names at her till she was all the way down the road. Jimmy said he was sorry he came out and caused me trouble. I said I was glad he had come out because I wanted to see him so bad. I said it didn't matter to me what old lady Sarah said because I didn't like her anyways and I didn't care what she said or what she thought. I told him to thank Caroline and Edna and Amos for the presents and to tell them I was sorry I had no presents for them but I'd make it up next year.

Jimmy said I should write to him at the butcher's because he wasn't going to quit until Caroline moved away and he'd let me know when that was and send the address so that as soon as I was able I could come and live with them. I almost cried when Jimmy left.

I was ashamed to ever go to town because of Sarah and what she'd say about me to the people there in town. I was sorry that it wasn't March and I could go to New York and live with Caroline and Jimmy, and away from Sarah and the people of the town.

I hardly ever went to town. I'd be so tired of the same old cans of things, I hardly ate and I wasn't feeling much like eating. When it was not too cold for walking I walked the hill up to the motel and then back further to the fields. It was way back from the road and I didn't feel no eyes but God's on me.

The ground crunched with ice under my feet and my footprints froze and I could follow them back or come again and see where I had been before.

Only my footsteps frozen in the ice, only my voice singing if I sang when I walked, only my voice screaming when I screamed in the hut. No one heard the screaming, the screams hit the walls and hit my ears. I screamed with all the screams I had in me when the Pearl tore out. I screamed from being scared and I screamed from the hurt and the not knowing what to do and when I stopped the Pearl started and kept up crying until I fed it with my milk.

It was not white and round, my Pearl. It was a sack of grey and from the grey, skinny arms and legs, and a face red and crying, and hair, black hair, long coarse black hair streaming from her head and her scalp was red showing through. It was not like Ma's, pink and soft and blonde.

I could almost see the black hair growing on her arms like his and the dark skin. She was a dark Pearl, my Pearl, a dark sucking Pearl.

It was warm with the oven going and the heat

and the hot water steaming in pots while I bathed the slime away. I wanted to bathe the blood away from me. I wanted to wash away the sweat that clung like oil and stunk, but I could only wash her and wrap her in a towel and sleep and we slept both together in the bed.

The doctor did not come. The doctor did not know. Nobody came. Nobody knew. I was alone to feed her and wash her and sleep and sleep, between the cries that came from her round pearl mouth.

I could have called and they would all have come. I could've called the butcher's and Jimmy would have come, or Brooklyn and Willie'd come, even Sarah. I could've called Sarah and have her come and look at me and my Pearl that she called bastard.

I could have called the doctor and he'd have come, only it was too late. I climbed the hill, slipping on the ice and the pain came in the fields. Trying to run back, sliding down the hill, pulling my legs together against the pain. The door did not yet close when it came and I only had time to scream, not to phone, only to scream and get the knife and scream.

It was too much to eat, only to sleep, only to sleep between the cries. It was too much to think, too tired to think between the cries. There had to be thoughts thought out before they came. There had to be thoughts thought out only by me before they came and tried to tell me what to do.

It was here. I did not count the days. I did not know the months and it was here. It could not have been March because Willie was not here. The sun came and the wind and the nights but I did not count, only waking and eating and waking and sleeping until the pain came rocking through my belly.

I heard the women telling Ma about their times. I heard them giving full accounts of births. I heard them scaring one another with the things they said, only Ma didn't scare. She kept having them and she said she could squeeze them out like orange juice.

I never had no pain before. The time I scraped my leg down to the bone and the doctor sewed it up without no ether, that was no pain next to this.

Weary, weary, I could sleep a thousand days and a thousand nights. I could sleep with the lights out, in the dark with the wind moaning lonely near the door. I could sleep.

I could sleep standing, washing her small jerking arms, and pinning. I could sleep scrubbing, till my diaper's free of blood and hers is white and smelling right again. Sleeping while I wring the water out and twist the cloth between my hands and twist the sleep from out my eyes.

In the dark I heard her cry and pulled her close and let her suck. I lay still, never turning, sleeping stiff, never moving and she lay beside me wrapped in towels.

The cradle's empty. The little white rocking cradle stays empty in the corner. And the clothes, the knitted socks and fancy hats and sweaters stay neat, stacked neat in Willie's drawers.

A Pearl does not wear knits and bows. A Pearl does not need cradles.

I made a cradle of my arms. Looking at my Pearl and it moved. It was not round and white and splashed with rainbows. It was living, breathing, crying and the black hair fell against her face and spread out on my arm and tickled on my breast. The mouth sucked hard and I felt the sucking way down between my legs. Sucking and sleeping and I looked good and could see none of Ma or Pa or Torrence or Caroline or me or Jimmy or none of the rest in her. She was him and yet not him, something strange, something I never saw before, not him with the thick hairy arms and the wide nose and the hairy bristles growing on his chin. Small with skinny kicking arms and legs, and crying, not like Torrence ever cried, and strange like not belonging here with me. Strange, like not belonging anywhere.

Her eyes blinking at the sun, at the sky, and she did not cry, only blinking. There was no wind, only the water rolling on the beach, lapping, licking at the beach in a way that the sea and the sand make with a sound.

The water was not colder than the day and I did not shiver with the chill. She did not cry with the cold. She did not cry.

Looking at the sun, at the sky, licking at the salt, she did not cry. Bobbing. The blanket sogged and came undone and floated on the water.

I knelt, splintering sea shells, watching the wool stretch out and sink to the bottom.

She never cried as I, softly, gently, the water welling up and running from my eyes. Crying for her, my Pearl, my bastard Pearl. I cried for Ma and for Jimmy and for Willie. I couldn't cry for me. There was no crying left for me. There are no tears for oysters. There are no tears.

I could not give my Pearl to Willie. I could not give her to the cradle with the rockers and the flowers painted on the white. Willie was the cradle and the Wailing Whale and a whale-shaped pool, spitting fountains like a whale.

Ma did not want her and the shame. Ma did not want me or the shame. There in the city with the houses tall and the streets hard to your feet and all the people hanging from the windows, sitting on the stoops, wheeling carriages, sitting in the sunlight, sitting in the moonlight, talking, yelling, gossiping, it was shameful. It was sinful.

Here in the quiet there was nothing until the

milk man came, or a truck rode by and the driver waved and you waved back and saw the eyes. In the town there were eyes, all Sarah's eyes, thinking Sarah's kind of things. There is nowhere for a pearl but in the sea. There is no shame in the sea. There is no sin in the sea.

Willie would have made it right. Willie would have held it and played. Willie would have known the words to say. It would fit with Willie with the hair so dark and Stan would have built for it and worked for it. It was for Stan to love like he loved Willie.

But they were Jews. They were Jews.

I don't care really. Really! Really! Really! Willie is more than Caroline. I feel to Willie almost as I felt to Ma. Not for myself I don't care but for Jimmy and Ma and Pa and Paul and Edna and Caroline and the rest. They would hate me, and the priests and the nuns, they would hate me too.

I will not go to them, in the city, with the bricks and the bricks and the bricks. Chimneys shooting soot and smoke, millions of chimneys smoking up the sky. And the buildings, clinging close, shutting out the sun and the air to breathe. Choking, in the dust with the horns honking and the tires screeching and the dust clinging to the street and the sides of buildings till the city's grey.

Grey city. There is no sunset and no sunrise. Great white puffs, pure white puffs falling from the sky, and the sky is not so blue, is not so high. The sky is not this sky that hangs over a grey city.

There is the sky to watch and to know. There is the sun that led me out and warmed me to the beach and made her stare at the brightness till she blinked.

She was soft, her head soft and I held it softly in my hand. My arms the cradle, rocking in my arms. And I sang like Ma sang, words and sounds I knew not what they meant, but she did. She sort of smiled, staring with her eyes, black eyes, and her fists kept going.

She held my finger in her fists, skinny tiny fingers, and she held on tight, squeezing her fingers to a fist. Her mouth found her fist and sucked. My sucking Pearl.

She was never mine to keep. I am too young. I am not like Ma. I could never be a mother. I could not go to Jimmy and be his mother, even.

Caroline wanted me. Caroline wrote. Caroline was alone in a room in the city and she was mad at Ma because Ma threw her out before it was time to graduate, and Jimmy stayed behind with Ma. She wanted me to come to her, alone.

I never answered. I never wrote and told her nothing.

I meant to write to Willie. I tried to write to Willie. I wanted to write and tell her all about the Pearl. I wanted to say she was hers. I wanted to tell Willie she could have the Pearl. I wanted to tell Willie that's what I wanted, but I couldn't. I couldn't say to Willie, "You've got to bring her up not to be a Jew." I couldn't say it. I couldn't.

I owed it to Willie. I owed her the living free and all the food and for being Willie. The Pearl was hers, come from her beach, from her bed. She drank Willie's milk from out my breasts. Willie spent the winter sewing baby things and knitting stitches for the Pearl, while I spent my winter kneading bread. It belonged to Willie but it grew inside of me, and I was not made like Willie. Willie was not confirmed like me.

I could give Willie my blood. I could pick all

the clams on the beach and chop wood from end-
less trees and give her every bit of money saved.
And I would be her sister and love her like a sister
does. But I couldn't give her Pearl and then let
Pearl be damned.

It was too much to let her be a bastard and let
her soul be damned.

It is too much to sit and watch the tide come
in. I watch the heavens and try to see her soul rise
up. My knees are sore from kneeling on the cottage
floor and on the sand, praying, praying. I shall be
damned, burning. The prayers burning in my
mouth, the prayers burning in my chest. I can feel
my soul shrivel up inside of me.

I would be the sea. I would be the sand and the
wind and the shells, dead and dying on the beach.
I would be the oyster huddled round my Pearl. I
would be the rain and the gull and I would be the
fish swimming and I would be anything but me.

I would be bones decaying. I would be a tree
chopped down. I would be a blade of grass chewed
by cows. I would be ore melting, steaming on a
furnace floor. I would be the bird with its feathers
plucked for a grand lady's hat. I would be the furry

thing skinned for the grand lady's coat. I would if I could be blind and never see the sea that brought this grief to me.

I came wanting. I came loving. I came needing. I came hungering and it filled my mouth with sand.

I sit and watch and it comes in lapping. It comes in coaxing, licking at my toes as if it doesn't know. As if it doesn't know like God knows how it happened on this beach. As if it didn't see like God saw how he tore my flesh and me. As if it didn't feel like God felt my Pearl drowning in its sea.

Maybe the sea is sorry. Maybe it comes in licking, never knowing. Maybe it is innocent as me when I first saw this sea.

It was not the sea who smashed the gull. It was not the sea who came in smashing me. It is not the sea that made me Catholic and Willie Jew. It is not the sea that swept inside and grew and grew.

I sit watching. I can only sit and watch the tide come in. I can only sit and watch the water for a sign. I could not say the things that needed saying when the kerchief came with seaweed and wrapped around my toes. The red wrapped with brown and green and black around my toes, and I could not move my hands or free my feet. I could not pull away the weeds or lift my feet or cry or pray or press up the square I wrapped my Pearly in.

I could only sit watching. There are no words for oysters. There are no sins and there are no sorrows and there are no souls for oysters.